D

CCEA A2
BIOLOGY EXAM PRACTICE

COLOURPOINT
EDUCATIONAL

Print ISBN: 978 1 78073 279 4

eBook ISBN: 978 1 78073 300 5

First Edition
Second Impression, 2022

Layout and design: April Sky Design
Printed by: GPS Colour Graphics Ltd, Belfast

The Author

James Napier is a former Vice-Principal in a large Northern Ireland grammar school. Dr Napier has written and co-written, a number of GCSE and 'A' level Biology and Science textbooks supporting the work of teachers and students in Northern Ireland. He has also published a range of popular science books throughout the areas of genetics and evolution.

The author would like to thank Jacqueline Gray for her very useful review of the manuscript of this book prior to publication.

COLOURPOINT EDUCATIONAL

Colourpoint Educational
An imprint of Colourpoint Creative Ltd
Colourpoint House
Jubilee Business Park
21 Jubilee Road
Newtownards
County Down
Northern Ireland
BT23 4YH

Tel: 028 9182 0505
E-mail: sales@colourpoint.co.uk
Website: www.colourpoint.co.uk

Publisher's Note: This book has been written to help students preparing for the A2 Level Biology specification from CCEA. While Colourpoint Educational and the author have taken every care in its production, we are not able to guarantee that the book is completely error-free. Additionally, while the book has been written to closely match the CCEA specification, it is the responsibility of each candidate to satisfy themselves that they have fully met the requirements of the CCEA specification prior to sitting an exam set by that body. For this reason, and because specifications change with time, we strongly advise every candidate to avail of a qualified teacher and to check the contents of the most recent specification for themselves prior to the exam. Colourpoint Creative Ltd therefore cannot be held responsible for any errors or omissions in this book or any consequences thereof.

Health and Safety: This book describes practical tasks or experiments that are either useful or required for the course. These must only be carried out in a school setting under the supervision of a qualified teacher. It is the responsibility of the school to ensure that students are provided with a safe environment in which to carry out the work. Where it is appropriate, they should consider reference to CLEAPPS.

CONTENTS

Introduction

As with the *Biology for CCEA AS Exam Practice* workbook, this A2 version gives students the opportunity to practise typical examination questions and check their answers against a mark scheme available on the Colourpoint website www.colourpointeducational.com. In this book, answer space is provided for all questions, except for the Section B essays which appear in the A2 1 and A2 2 sections.

The workbook is divided into three units, there being a unit for each of A2 1, A2 2 and A2 3. Within the A2 1 and A2 2 units the questions are arranged by topic in chapters that mirror the content of the textbook *Biology for CCEA A2*, by the same author and publisher.

The content covered at A2 is different from AS and therefore the A2 papers are different. However, there are other differences with A2 papers. They are longer, they contain more marks, and there is a different Assessment Objective (AO) balance. Additionally, there is synoptic assessment with core knowledge from AS required in some questions. These points will be covered in the next few paragraphs, as will some other features unique to the A2 examination papers.

As with the AS course, it is important that students have an excellent understanding of all the specification, including the mathematical skills required (Section 4.7) and the common command terms used in written examinations (Appendix 1).

Types of questions

As with the AS papers, questions can be divided into three broad categories:

- **Assessment Objective 1 (AO1)** questions test knowledge and understanding of specification content. Command terms such as 'define' or 'describe' are typically used in AO1 questions.
- **Assessment Objective 2 (AO2)** questions involve application of knowledge. They include calculations and those which are set in unfamiliar contexts. Typically, AO2 questions involve a more rigorous testing of understanding and transferable skills than that

required in AO1 questions.
- **Assessment Objective 3 (AO3)** questions are those questions in which students analyse, interpret and evaluate information and make judgements and/or reach conclusions. AO3 questions often involve candidates interpreting data in tables or graphs, or even in text.

However, what is different is that in A2 examinations the relative proportions of the question types are different. Across the A2 suite of examinations, there is proportionally more testing of AO2 and AO3 skills. This means that A2 papers have a greater emphasis on skills such as answering questions based on unfamiliar settings, data handling and evaluating data. Consequently, there will be proportionally fewer questions requiring the relatively straightforward recall of information.

Mathematical skills

Mathematical skills required in GCE Biology, and in A2 examinations in particular, are clearly outlined in the specification (**Section 4.7**). If you refer to the specification, you will notice that some of the mathematical skills are highlighted in bold – these skills are required for A2 only (not required at AS) and therefore, are likely to be tested in A2 papers. While the use of logarithmic scales could be tested in any of the three A2 papers, statistics questions (questions involving chi-square, the t-test and/or 95% confidence limits) will only appear in A2 2 or A2 3 papers. For many of the questions involving statistics in this workbook you will require access to statistics tables (sheets), and these can be found in **Appendix 2** of the specification.

Synoptic knowledge and assessment

A2 papers can test synoptic knowledge, understanding and skills – this means that content covered earlier in the course can be required in A2 papers. Students should not be concerned about this as synoptic assessment will primarily focus on the core concepts that are crucial to a good all-round understanding of 'A' level Biology. For example, students cannot fully understand ultrafiltration from the glomerulus into the Bowman's capsule and reabsorption from the proximal convoluted tubule unless they have a solid understanding of osmosis and active transport (which are covered in AS 1). Similarly, an understanding of mitochondrial structure (also covered in AS 1) is necessary in understanding the biochemistry of respiration. However, synoptic assessment will normally only involve those topics and skills which are necessary in understanding A2 content.

Other ways to maximise marks

By reviewing the online Chief Examiner's Reports in the GCE Biology area at www.ccea.org.uk , the most frequent misconceptions, the topics which are poorly understood and examples of poor examination techniques are highlighted. Useful guidance is also disseminated in the webinars and other support material. The wise student is a student who is familiar with areas where marks are typically lost in questions and papers and avoids making the mistakes that many others do.

Mark schemes

As stated in the *Biology for CCEA AS Exam Practice* workbook, mark schemes are not finalised until examiners have had a chance to review the range of answers provided by candidates. Sometimes, unexpected answers appear which deserve credit but were not in the initial draft mark scheme. Answers such as these can then be added as alternatives to the mark scheme before the marking begins if appropriate.

The same principle applies to the mark schemes for the questions in this book. While a range of alternative answers are provided for many questions, it is probable that some creditworthy answers are not included for some of the question parts. Additionally, for some questions the phrase 'other appropriate response' is given as an alternative, particularly for those questions where a wide range of creditworthy answers are possible.

The mark scheme (the answers) for this workbook are available online. Visit www.colourpointeducational.com and search for *Biology Exam Practice for CCEA A2*. The page for this book will contain instructions for downloading the mark scheme. If you have any difficulties please contact Colourpoint.

Good luck!

Unit A2 1: Physiology, Co-ordination and Control, and Ecosystems

Chapter 1 – Homeostasis and the Kidney

1 The two functions of the kidney are excretion and osmoregulation.

   (a) Define the term 'excretion'.

   _____

   _____ [1]

   (b) Describe the role of the following structures in kidney function.

   basement membrane _____

   _____

   _____

   _____ [2]

   collecting duct _____

   _____

   _____

   _____ [2]

2 The structure, position and arrangement of the glomeruli blood vessels ensure that they are highly adapted for the ultrafiltration of blood into the Bowman's capsule. State **three** of these adaptations.

   1. _____

   2. _____

   3. _____ [3]

3 In the kidney, glucose is filtered from the glomerulus into the nephron before being reabsorbed back into the blood. The reabsorption of glucose takes place in the proximal convoluted tubule.

(a) The diagram below represents an epithelial cell in the wall of the proximal convoluted tubule.

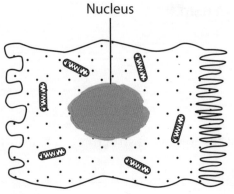

Nucleus

(i) Add an arrow to the diagram to show the direction of glucose reabsorption into the cell. [1]

(ii) Using the diagram, state and explain **one** way in which the cell is adapted for glucose reabsorption.

_____

_____

_____

_____ [2]

(iii) Glucose reabsorption involves both facilitated diffusion and active transport. Explain why each method is involved.

_____

_____

_____

_____

_____

_____

_____

_____ [3]

(b) The graph below shows the relationship between blood glucose concentration and the amount of glucose reabsorbed by nephrons in the human kidney.

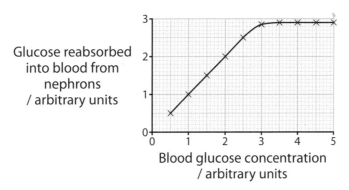

Glucose reabsorbed into blood from nephrons / arbitrary units

Blood glucose concentration / arbitrary units

(i) Suggest why the graph shows no values less than 0.5 arbitrary units.

_____

_____ [1]

(ii) Describe fully the results for a blood glucose concentration of 0.5 – 2.5 arbitrary units.

_____

_____

_____

_____

_____

_____ [2]

(iii) In terms of cell membrane structure and function, suggest **one** reason for the results shown for blood glucose concentrations above 3 arbitrary units.

_____

_____

_____ [1]

(c) Around 70% of the total water reabsorbed in the kidney is reabsorbed in the proximal tubule. Name the process involved in water reabsorption and explain how the reabsorption of glucose aids this process.

_____

_____

_____

_____

_____ [2]

4 (a) The diagram below represents part of a nephron.

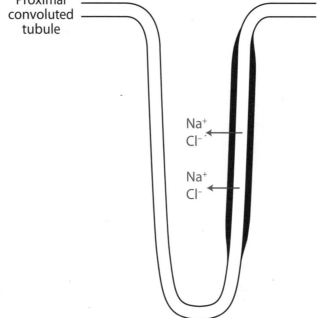

(i) Identify the part of the nephron shown.

_____ [1]

(ii) Name the region of the kidney within which this structure is found.

_____ [1]

(iii) Using the information provided and your knowledge of kidney function, explain the role of the structure shown in the reabsorption of water.

_____

_____

_____

_____

_____

_____

_____

_____

_____

_____ [4]

(b) Antidiuretic hormone (ADH) also plays an important role in osmoregulation. Explain the role of ADH.

_____

_____

_____

_____

_____

_____

_____ [3]

5 The kidney is an important homeostatic organ in the body.

   (a) Define the term 'homeostasis'.

   _____

   _____

   _____ [1]

   (b) The diagram below summarises the role of the kidney in osmoregulation.

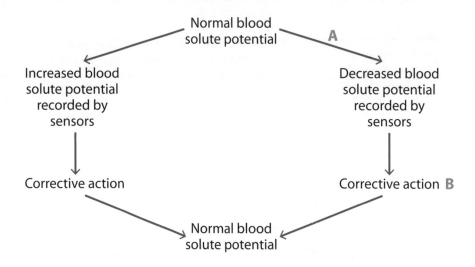

   (i) State the location of the sensors (osmoreceptors).

   _____ [1]

   (ii) Suggest how the change in blood solute potential at **A** may have occurred.

   _____ [1]

(iii) Describe the corrective action which occurs, represented by the letter **B** in the diagram.

_____

_____

_____

_____

_____

_____

_____

_____ [3]

(iv) As the sensors detect the blood solute concentration returning to normal, the corrective action is reduced and eventually stopped. State the term given to this process.

_____ [1]

1 **(a)** The graph below shows how the antibody concentration in the blood of an individual changes over time following initial and subsequent infections by the same type of pathogen.

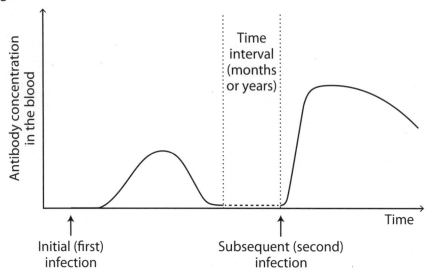

(i) Describe fully the reason for the delay in antibody production following the initial infection.

_____

_____

_____

_____

_____ [2]

(ii) Explain the differences between the response to the subsequent infection and the initial infection.

_____

_____

_____

_____

_____ [2]

(b) Describe the role of antibodies in combatting pathogens.

_____

_____

_____

_____

_____ [2]

Polymorphs are usually involved in the final destruction of pathogens following antibody action.

(c) Name and describe the process involved.

Name _____

_____

_____

_____

_____ [3]

2 Write the most appropriate terms to match the statements below.

• the type of immunity that mainly involves T-lymphocytes _____

• the type of cells that directly synthesise antibodies _____

• the type of (long term) immunity produced by memory cells _____ [3]

3 Influenza is a common infectious disease that affects millions of people each year. The flu virus is spherical, 100 – 200 nm in diameter, and has an RNA core. Infection is spread by coughing and sneezing.

The flu virus has many 'spike-like' proteins on its surface which act as antigens.

(a) Define precisely the term 'antigen'.

_____

_____

_____[1]

(b) When an individual is infected with a flu virus, it enters the cells lining the nasal cavity and respiratory passages where it replicates, causing cell destruction as it passes from cell to cell.

The presence of the virus causes macrophages and other phagocytes to invade infected tissue. At this early stage of immune response, the macrophages release cytokines which bring about an increase in T and B cells.

(i) Among the cells which increase in number are killer and helper T-cells. Describe the roles of killer (cytotoxic) and helper T-cells in an immune response.

_____

_____

_____

_____

_____ [2]

(ii) Using the information provided, describe the role of cytokines in the immune response.

_____

_____ [1]

(iii) Using the information provided, suggest why cytokines are suitable for use as biomarkers for the detection of infection.

_____

_____

_____

_____

_____ [2]

The protein molecules on the surface of the flu virus frequently change as a result of mutation, with the result that there is usually a number of different strains of flu at any one time in a region.

(c) Using the information provided, suggest and explain why an individual can have a flu vaccination and still develop flu a few months later.

_____

_____

_____

_____ [2]

(d) Due to a combination of fast rates of mutation and ease of spread, the flu virus has often resulted in flu epidemics.
Define the term 'epidemic'.

_____

_____

_____ [1]

4 (a) 'Herd' immunity is the concept that if a high percentage of the population is vaccinated against a particular infectious disease, then the population as a whole is protected against that disease. For measles, it is thought the percentage vaccinated to achieve 'herd' immunity needs to be well above 90%. Herd immunity is necessary to protect those individuals who cannot be vaccinated, e.g. very young babies and people who are immunosuppressed.

(i) Suggest why an individual who is not vaccinated is unlikely to suffer from an infectious disease in a population where there is 'herd' immunity to that particular disease.

_____

_____ [1]

(ii) Describe how vaccination stimulates the immune system into protection against disease.

_____

_____

_____

_____

_____

_____

_____

_____ [3]

(iii) Explain why the immunity produced by vaccination is described as 'active'.

_____

_____[1]

(b) Measles used to be a common childhood infectious disease in the British Isles. Since the introduction of the MMR vaccination, many areas of the country have been effectively 'disease free'.

However, there have been occasional isolated outbreaks of measles. For example, in 2013 in Swansea, south Wales, well over one thousand people caught measles.

In this area there had been a relatively low uptake of the MMR vaccination (<70%) mainly due to 'health scares' in the local media.

(i) Suggest what message the 'health scare' gave.

_____

_____ [1]

When an individual is infected with measles, the virus enters cells in the lower respiratory tract. After multiplying in these cells, the rapidly increasing number of viruses enter macrophages (which become 'antigen-presenting' cells) where further multiplication takes place. In due course the viruses enter the blood stream and spread throughout the body.

(ii) Describe the cell-mediated response to the presence of antigens on 'antigen-presenting cells'.

_____

_____

_____

_____

_____

_____

_____ [3]

(iii) Using the information provided, explain why the immune response to measles infection will involve both cell-mediated and antibody-mediated responses.

_____

_____

_____ [1]

5 (a) The partially completed table below shows the results of transfusions between different ABO blood groups. (✓ = no reaction; X = agglutination)

Blood group of donor	Blood group of recipient			
	A	B	AB	O
A	✓	X	✓	X
B			✓	
AB			✓	
O			✓	

(i) Complete the table above. [3]

(ii) Using the information in the table, describe and explain why blood group **AB** is described as the 'universal recipient'.

_____

_____

_____

_____ [2]

(iii) In the context of transfusion incompatibility, describe what is meant by the term 'agglutination' and describe a possible consequence of this.

_____

_____

_____

_____ [2]

(b) The rhesus antigen (antigen D) may also occur on the surface membrane of red blood cells.

Individuals with the rhesus antigen are described as being Rhesus positive (Rh⁺) and those without are Rhesus negative (Rh⁻). Anti-rhesus (anti-D) antibodies do not usually occur in individuals.

(i) A mother who is Rh⁻ was found to have anti-D antibodies in her blood. Explain how this is most likely to have arisen.

_____

_____

_____

_____

_____ [2]

(ii) In subsequent pregnancies in this mother, the foetus could be at significant risk unless the mother receives specific medical intervention.

Explain how this risk could arise.

_____

_____

_____

_____

_____

_____

_____ [3]

6 Antibiotics have been used to treat bacterial infections since they were first used in the 1940s. However, a significant problem is that 'inappropriate' use of antibiotics has encouraged the development of antibiotic resistance in bacteria.

(a) Suggest **two** examples of 'inappropriate' use of antibiotics.

1. _____

_____

2. _____

_____ [2]

(b) In an investigation of resistance in a bacterial population subjected to an antibiotic, the percentages of bacteria which were resistant and non-resistant were recorded over time. The results are shown in the graph below.

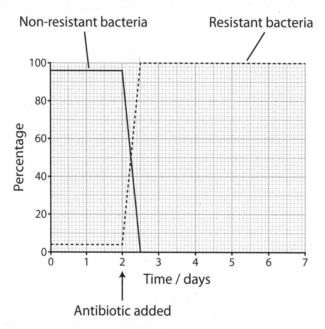

(i) Calculate the percentage increase per hour of resistant bacteria in the 12 hours immediately after the antibiotic was added.
(Show your working.)

_____ % hour⁻¹ [2]

(ii) Describe and explain the results shown.

_____

_____

_____

_____

_____

_____

_____

_____

_____ [3]

(c) Many different types of antibiotics are used in medicine. For example, some target the cell membrane in bacteria by making it fully permeable; others break down the cell wall and others target bacterial metabolism. The antibiotic erythromycin works by damaging bacterial ribosomes and preventing protein synthesis.

Using your understanding of cell structure, suggest why erythromycin can destroy bacterial ribosomes yet have no effect on the ribosomes in the cells of human patients taking this antibiotic.

_____

_____ [1]

(d) Many of the new antibiotics developed over recent decades have been discovered in soil bacteria. Suggest and explain why soil bacteria may be a valuable source of antibiotics.

_____

_____

_____

_____

_____ [2]

7 Sars-CoV-2 (coronavirus) is the flu-like virus responsible for the Covid-19 pandemic that affected most countries throughout the world in the year 2020. Scientists first became aware of this virus and its effect on humans in late 2019 as infections and deaths spread rapidly in a region of China. During the year 2020 many thousands of people died from this infection in the United Kingdom alone.

A common method of infection is inhaling the virus suspended in the aerosols created by the coughing and sneezing of an infected individual.

In the UK, following a rapid increase in infections and deaths due to Covid-19, individuals were asked to remain at home where possible, and where it was necessary to leave home such as for essential work or to buy food, to practise 'social distancing' which included staying at least two metres away from other people. Individuals who displayed symptoms of the condition were asked to 'self-isolate' – remain at home – and keep away from others over the time period they were likely to remain infectious. The self-isolation of doctors and nurses who had developed symptoms of the disease became a particular issue as this meant that they could not work for at least one week even though they may have had recovered (and not be infectious) or may not even have had the disease in the first place.

A high proportion of the patients who died from Covid-19 were elderly and/or individuals with underlying health conditions such as diabetes or heart disease.

(a) (i) Using the information provided, explain the importance of 'social distancing' in reducing infection rates.

_____

_____

_____ [1]

(ii) In terms of how the body defends against disease, suggest why it was mainly people who were elderly or had underlying health conditions who were most seriously affected.

_____

_____ [1]

(b) As coronavirus had only very recently infected humans for the first time, in the early months of 2020 scientists raced to develop appropriate medical tests specific to this virus. This included research to produce a test that would show the presence of coronavirus antigens (an antigen test to detect the presence of coronavirus nucleic acid or surface markers) in the nasal cavity or upper respiratory tract, and a separate test that would show the presence of antibodies to the coronavirus in an individual's blood (antibody test).

(i) Describe the information that each of these tests would provide for medical staff.

Presence of antigens _____

_____

Presence of antibodies _____

_____ [2]

(ii) For each test, suggest **one** benefit that having this information would provide.

Antigen test _____

_____

_____

Antibody test _____

_____

_____ [2]

(iii) Scientists are aware that the best long-term approach to avoid further epidemics or pandemics involving Covid-19 is to develop a vaccine for the disease. Apart from providing protection against disease, suggest **two** features that a successful vaccine should possess.

1. _____

_____

2. _____

_____ [2]

(c) During the Covid-19 pandemic, scientists became aware that many seriously ill patients had a very high level of cytokines in their blood (referred to as a 'cytokine storm').

State the function of cytokines in immunity and suggest an explanation for the very high level of cytokines in the blood of these patients.

_____

_____

_____

_____ [2]

(d) Before infecting humans, the coronavirus crossed the species barrier from some type of animal before then being transmitted among humans. This recent transfer to humans is part of the reason why the coronavirus has been so harmful.

(i) Suggest **one** reason why a virus which has recently crossed the species barrier is likely to be more harmful to humans than one which has been infecting humans for many years.

_____

_____

_____ [1]

(ii) In general, viruses are more likely to cause pandemics than bacteria. Suggest **two** reasons for this.

1. _____

2. _____ [2]

Chapter 3 – Coordination and Control in Plants

1 State the most appropriate word or phrase that matches each of the following descriptions.

• the pigment that exists in two interconvertible forms and can promote flowering in plants

_____

• a plant in which the onset of flowering is triggered by increasing day length

_____

• the plant growth substance which promotes cell division

_____

• the part of a plant where growth is stimulated by gibberellin

_____ [4]

2 (a) Name the part of a plant which contains phytochrome.

_____ [1]

(b) An investigation was carried out to determine the photoperiod necessary to promote flowering in a plant species. The results are shown in the table below.

Length of continuous light period/hours	Length of continuous dark period/hours	Flowering outcome
14	10	no flowering
13	11	no flowering
12	12	flowering
11	13	flowering
10	14	flowering

(i) Describe the evidence which indicates that this is a 'short-day' plant.

_____

_____

_____ [1]

(ii) In terms of phytochrome, describe what causes the onset of flowering in short-day plants.

_____

_____

_____

_____

_____ [2]

(c) The following diagram shows the effect of different light regimes on a long-day plant.

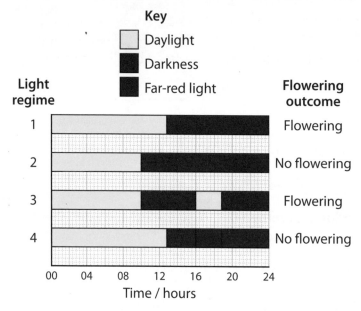

(i) In terms of phytochrome conversions, explain why the plant flowers in light regime **3**.

_____

_____

_____ [1]

(ii) The total length of daylight is the same in light regimes **1** and **4**, yet flowering occurs in light regime **1** but not in light regime **4**. Explain why.

_____

_____

_____

_____

_____

_____

_____

_____

_____

_____ [3]

(d) A species which produces flowers that are commercially popular normally flowers in November. The species is a short-day plant. A grower wishes to delay flowering in this species until mid-December in order that flowers will be available for the Christmas market.

Describe how this could be done. Explain your answer.

_____

_____

_____

_____

_____

_____

_____ [3]

3 Growth in plant stems is a consequence of both cell division and cell elongation. The parts of the stem where division and elongation occur are shown in the diagram below.

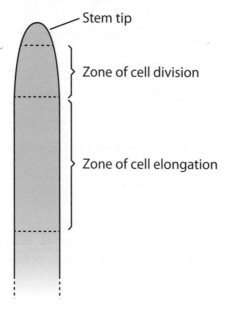

(a) Auxin is one of a number of plant growth substances (hormones) which promote growth. In an experiment to investigate the effect of auxin on plant cells, auxin was added to a group of cells which had just completed division. Cell sizes before and after auxin application are represented in the diagram below.

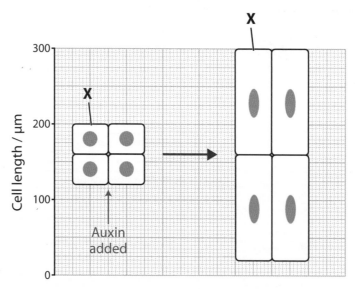

(i) Calculate the percentage increase in length of cell **X** after the auxin was added. (Show your working.)

_____ % [2]

(ii) Apart from the increase in cell length, give **one** other difference between the two groups of cells.

_____

_____ [1]

(iii) Suggest why it was important to use cells which had just undergone division in this investigation.

_____

_____ [1]

Auxin acts by loosening the connections between different components of the cell wall. This makes the cell wall more flexible, allowing it to stretch. Turgor pressure, following this increase in wall flexibility, leads to the greater cell length.

(iv) It has been demonstrated that the water potential of plant cells decreases as a consequence of auxin application. Suggest the importance of this in stem elongation.

_____

_____

_____ [1]

(b) The graph below shows how cell length changes moving further from the stem tip. Cell auxin concentration is also shown.

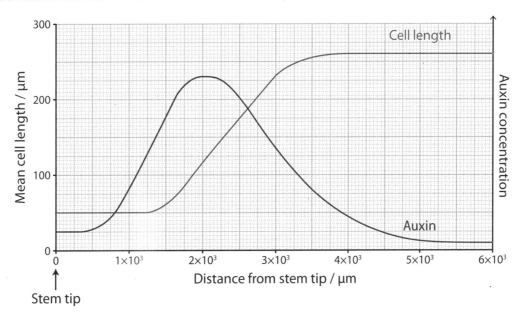

(i) With the letter **Y** identify, on the horizontal axis, the distance from the stem tip where the zone of cell division ends. [1]

(ii) Describe and explain the results shown.

_____

_____

_____

_____

_____

_____

_____

_____

_____

_____ [4]

(c) Plant growth substances have a number of similarities with animal hormones. State **one** similarity.

_____

_____ [1]

Chapter 4 – Neurones and Synapses

1 (a) Give the most appropriate term to describe the statements below.

  • the very fine extensions through which nerve impulses enter a neurone

  _____

  • the structure at the end of a neurone which makes and secretes neurotransmitter

  _____

  • the very small gaps between Schwann cells in a myelinated neurone

  _____   [3]

  (b) (i) Describe what is meant by the term 'refractory period'.

  _____

  _____

  _____ [1]

  (ii) Suggest **one** advantage of neurones having a 'refractory period'.

  _____

  _____ [1]

2 (a) The diagram below represents a section through part of a nerve containing several neurones.

  (i) In terms of speed of nerve impulse, place the neurones **W**, **X** and **Y** in order.

  Fastest _____ _____ _____ Slowest   [1]

(ii) Neurone **Z** is myelinated. Explain the difference in appearance with other myelinated neurones.

_____

_____ [1]

(iii) Temperature is a factor which affects the speed of impulse transmission. When comparing speed of impulse in the neurones represented above, suggest why temperature will **not** be an important factor.

_____

_____ [1]

(b) The diagram below represents a nerve impulse. Values on the y-axis represent the potential inside the membrane relative to the outside.

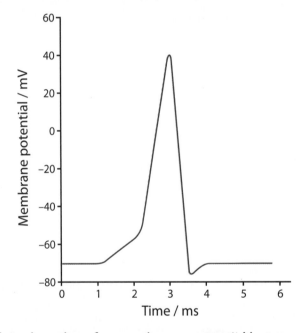

Describe and explain the values for membrane potential between 0 – 3 ms.

_____

_____

_____

_____

_____

_____

_____

_____

_____

_____

_____

_____ [5]

3 **(a)** The diagram below represents a typical reflex arc, such as that involved in the 'withdrawal' reflex.

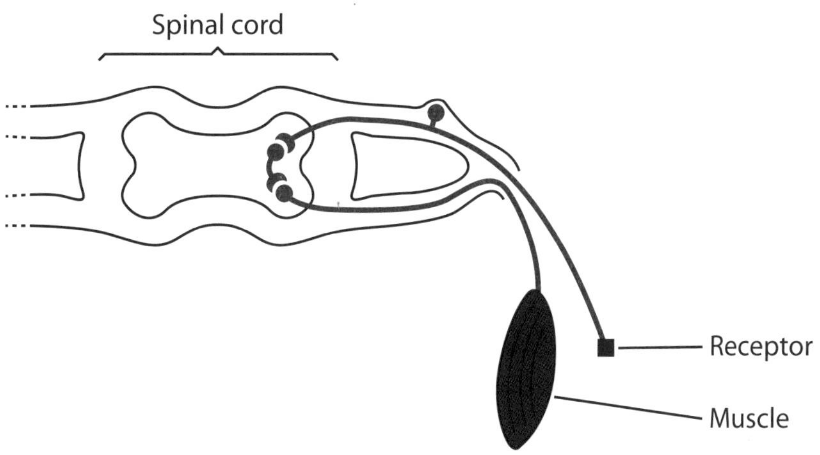

Spinal cord

Receptor

Muscle

(i) On the diagram, with the letter **X,** identify the cell body of a neurone. [1]

(ii) Add an arrow to one of the neurones to show the direction of nervous transmission. [1]

The reflex arc shown has three neurones and therefore only two synapses. Some reflex arcs, such as the 'knee jerk' reflex have only two neurones.

(iii) Suggest an advantage of a reflex having two rather than three neurones. Explain your answer.

_____

_____

_____

_____ [2]

Separate neurones extend from those in reflex arcs through the spinal cord and up to the brain.

(iv) Suggest **one** function of these neurones.

_____

_____ [1]

(b) The diagram below represents a synapse.

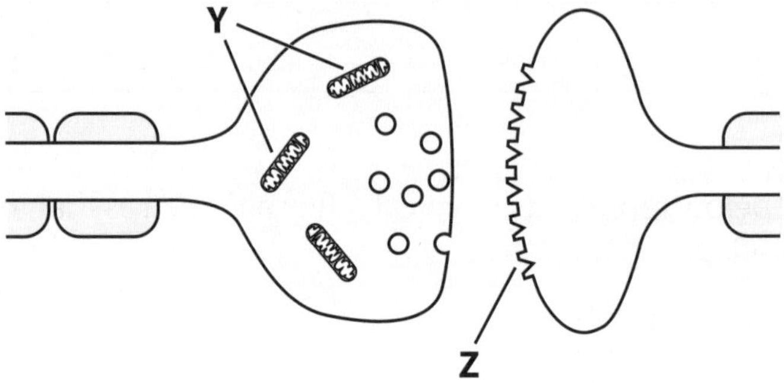

(i) Identify the structures labelled **Y** and **Z**.

Y _____

Z _____ [2]

(ii) Describe the sequence of events between a nerve impulse arriving at a synaptic bulb and the generation of an excitatory post-synaptic potential (EPSP).

_____

_____

_____

_____

_____

_____

_____

_____

_____

_____

_____

_____ [5]

(c) The synaptic cleft width between most neurones ranges between 20 – 40 nm.
($1 \text{ nm} = 1 \times 10^{-9}$ m.) If the speed of synaptic transmission is 0.50 ms^{-1}, use the
information provided to calculate the shortest time it will take neurotransmitter to cross
a synapse. Give your answer in standard form.

(Show your working.)

_____ s [3]

4 (a) The diagram below represents two neurones forming synaptic junctions with a
dendron on a motor neurone. The synapse E1 is excitatory and H1 is inhibitory.

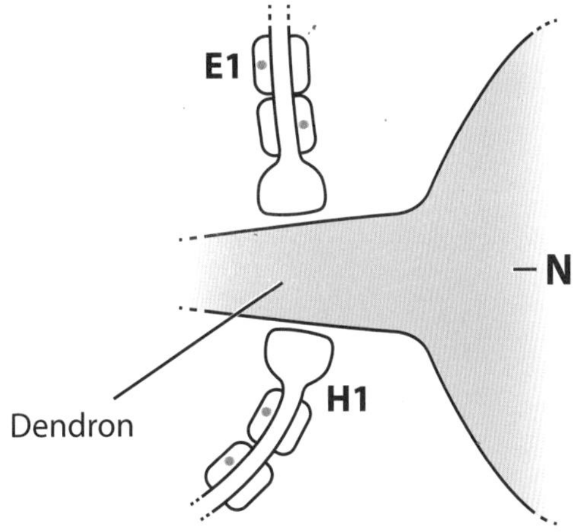

(i) On the diagram, label (the position of) a post-synaptic membrane with the
letter **M**. [1]

(ii) Name the part of the motor neurone labelled **N**.

_____ [1]

(iii) Using the diagram, explain why it is possible for a nerve impulse arriving at the synaptic bulb of neurone E1 **not** to result in a nerve impulse being produced in the motor neurone.

_____

_____

_____

_____

_____

_____

_____

_____ [3]

(iv) Give **one** example of a neurotransmitter produced at an inhibitory synapse.

_____ [1]

Some synapses are electrical rather than chemical (where a chemical neurotransmitter is involved). In electrical synapses, an electrical charge passes across the synaptic cleft. The synaptic cleft in electrical synapses is around 4 nm wide, a much shorter gap than that found in a chemical synapse.

(b) Suggest **one** advantage of electrical synapses.

_____ [1]

Chapter 5 – The Eye and Muscle

1 (a) The diagram below shows how light rays from a near object are focused on the retina.

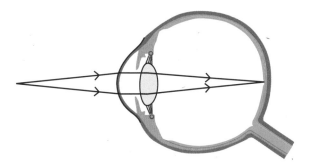

(i) Name the **two** parts of the eye where refraction of light occurs.

_____ and _____   [1]

(ii) Using the diagram, describe the changes that would take place within the eye to enable it to focus on a distant object after focusing on a near object (as in the diagram above).

_____

_____

_____

_____

_____

_____

_____

_____   [3]

(b) Most mammals have good depth perception. Describe how this is achieved.

_____

_____

_____

_____

_____ [2]

2 (a) With reference to vision, define the following terms.

visual acuity _____

_____

_____

retinal convergence _____

_____

_____

dark adaptation _____

_____

_____ [3]

(b) The human eye is sensitive to wavelengths (colours) across the visual spectrum.

   (i) In terms of photoreceptors, describe how this is achieved.

_____

_____

_____

_____

_____

_____

_____

_____ [3]

(ii) Colour blindness is a condition in which an individual is unable to distinguish between a small range of colours. Using your knowledge of photoreceptors, suggest an explanation for this.

_____

_____ [1]

3 The diagram below represents part of the retina.

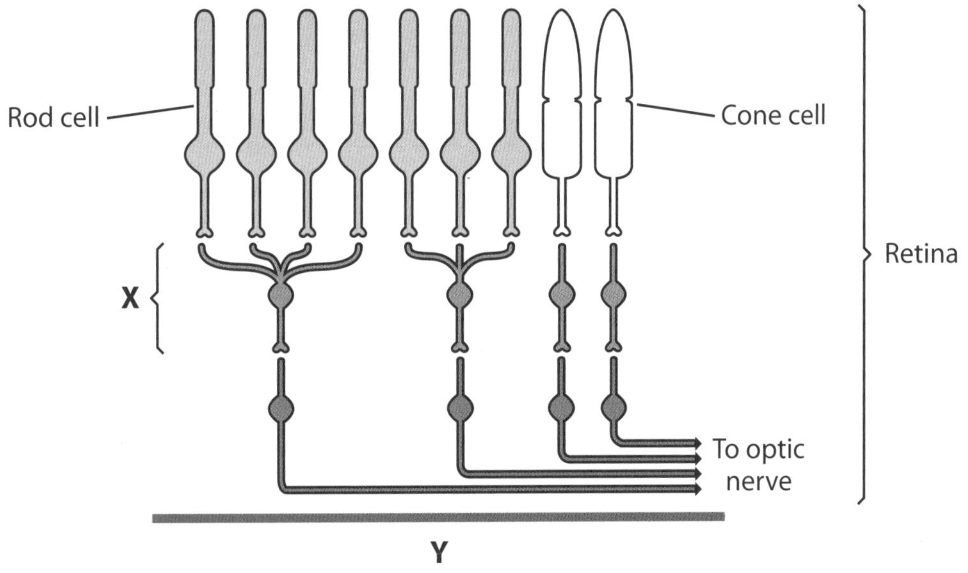

(a) **(i)** Identify the structures labelled **X**.

_____ [1]

(ii) Add an arrow to the diagram, to show the direction in which light enters the retina. [1]

(iii) Identify the part of the eye which would be found at position **Y**.

_____ [1]

(b) Using the diagram, explain how the arrangement of cells in the retina enables the eye to provide both high visual acuity (in high light levels) and high sensitivity (in low light levels).

_____

_____

_____

_____

_____

_____

_____

_____

_____

_____

_____

_____ [5]

4 (a) The diagram below shows how rods are distributed across the retina in humans.

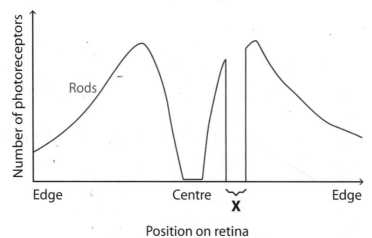

(i) Identify the part of the retina labelled **X**.

_____ [1]

(ii) Complete the diagram to show how cones are distributed across the retina. [2]

(iii) Peripheral vision is vision at the edge of our field of view. With reference to the distribution of photoreceptors, explain why in low illumination, human peripheral vision allows the identification of shapes and outlines but not their colour.

_____

_____

_____

_____

_____

_____

_____

_____

_____ [3]

(b) Nocturnal animals such as owls are active at night rather than during the day.

Suggest **two** ways in which the eyes of nocturnal animals are likely to be structurally different from the human eye.

1. _____

_____

2. _____

_____ [2]

5 (a) Distinguish between the terms 'muscle fibre' and 'myofibril'.

_____

_____

_____

_____

_____ [2]

(b) The diagram below represents two sarcomeres (and parts of adjacent sarcomeres) in a contracted state.

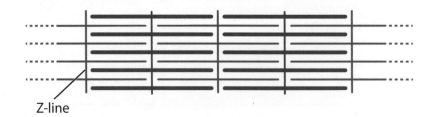

Z-line

(i) Using a labelled line, identify an actin filament on the diagram. [1]

(ii) State **two** changes that will be evident in the sarcomeres as the muscle **relaxes**.

1. _____

2. _____ [2]

(c) Myofibrillar myopathy is a muscle condition caused by gene mutations. The mutations lead to faults in sarcomere Z-lines (discs) in skeletal muscle.

(i) Suggest and explain the consequence of damage to sarcomere Z-lines.

_____

_____

_____

_____

_____ [2]

(ii) Myofibrillar myopathy also affects cardiac muscle but not smooth muscle.
Using your knowledge of skeletal, cardiac and smooth muscle, suggest why skeletal and cardiac muscle are affected but not smooth muscle.

_____

_____

_____ [1]

6 **(a)** The diagram below represents a small section of a sarcomere immediately before myosin heads attach to the actin filaments.

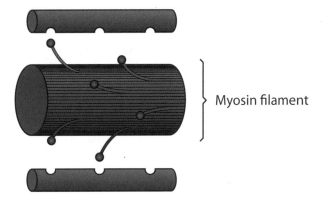

Myosin filament

(i) Add an arrow to the diagram to show the direction the actin filaments will move after the myosin heads are in place. [1]

(ii) Describe precisely what causes the actin filaments to move.

_____

_____

_____ [1]

(iii) State the role of ATP in muscle contraction.

_____

_____ [1]

(b) Tendons are structures that join muscles to bone. Tendons need to be securely attached to the bone and muscle and they also need to be strong. It is also important that they do not stretch.

(i) Using your understanding of muscle action, suggest why it is important that tendons do not stretch.

_____

_____

_____ [1]

(ii) Tendons are mainly composed of collagen fibres. Give **one** feature of collagen structure that makes it suitable for tendons.

_____

_____ [1]

Chapter 6 – Populations and Communities

1 **(a)** The graph below shows how the number of yeast cells in glucose solution in a beaker changed over time.

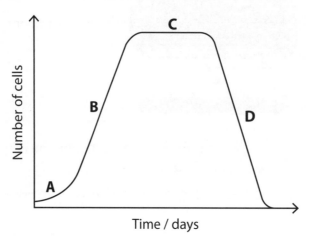

Using the graph, identify the stage or stages (**A** – **D**) where:

• the 'carrying capacity' of the population is achieved _____

• death rate > birth rate _____

• the population's 'biotic potential' is achieved _____

• the accumulation of waste has no effect on population growth _____

• there will be 'environmental resistance' _____   [5]

(b) Explain why semi-log graph paper is often used when plotting the change in numbers of microbes over time.

_____

_____

_____

_____

_____ [2]

2 **(a)** The partially completed table below summarises ways in which populations may interact.

Complete the table.

Interaction	Nature of relationship
competition	–/–
grazing	
parasitism	
	+/+

[3]

(b) Competition between two species often leads to the elimination of one species at the expense of the other (better competitor) species. Suggest why 'competition' is still described as an interaction in which both species suffer harm.

_____

_____

_____ [1]

3 The common periwinkle (*Littorina littorea*) is a snail commonly found on rocky shores. When covered by water, it feeds on algae encrusted to rock surfaces. A periwinkle can move more than a metre from its base to obtain food.

Periwinkles can live three or more years and when not feeding are normally found in rock crevices where they are protected against desiccation and predators.

(a) With reference to the periwinkle, describe what is meant by the term 'population'.

_____

_____ [1]

(b) The number of periwinkles on a large rock in the middle shore zone was investigated over a one-year period. The table below shows the number of periwinkles, and factors affecting this number, at the end of this period.

Factor	Number at end of one-year period
Total number on rock	55
Births	17
Deaths	14
Immigration	4
Emigration	5

In the context of this investigation, immigration refers to periwinkles not 'born' on the rock but which arrived there during the investigation; conversely, emigration refers to periwinkles that started life on the rock but moved to other parts of the shore during the investigation.

(i) Calculate the number of periwinkles on the rock at the start of the investigation. (Show your working.)

_____ [2]

(ii) Using the information provided, suggest **two** factors which would influence the 'carrying capacity' of the periwinkles on a rocky shore.

1. _____

2. _____ [2]

4 The photograph below shows the flowers of the plant parasite toothwort (*Lathraea squamaria*).

Credit: James Napier

Most of the plant grows underground with the flowers being the only part normally above ground, and these are only visible for a few weeks around April.

The plant has reduced scaly underground 'leaves' that do not contain chlorophyll. It is parasitic on the roots of woodland trees, using special structures called 'haustoria' that can penetrate roots to break down and absorb nutrients.

(a) Define the term 'parasite'.

_____

_____

_____ [1]

Toothwort is a very unusual plant in that it does not have chlorophyll and is therefore not an autotroph. Nonetheless, it is classified as a plant.

(b) Using your knowledge of classification, suggest **one** other feature, characteristic of plants, toothwort must have to be classified in this way.

_____ [1]

(c) Toothwort is parasitic on a range of trees including hazel, beech, sycamore and laurel.

   (i) Suggest the benefit to toothwort of having a range of host species.

   _____

   _____

   _____ [1]

An investigation was carried out to determine the host species of toothwort plants in a large wood. For consistency, it was agreed that the host tree was identified as the tree closest to a particular flower or group of flowers. The results are shown in the table below.

Host species	Number of trees of each species parasitised by toothwort
laurel	5
hazel	11
sycamore	1
beech	2
oak	1

(ii) Summarise the results shown.

_____

_____

_____

_____

_____

_____ [2]

(iii) The data in the table was based on probability of host species rather than absolute certainty. Explain why.

_____

_____

_____ [1]

(iv) Apart from your answer to part (iii), suggest **one** other reason why conclusions drawn from this investigation could not be considered totally reliable.

_____

_____

_____ [1]

5 The photograph below shows Giant Hogweed (*Heracleum mantegazzianum*) growing at a river's edge.

Credit: James Napier

(a) Giant Hogweed is not native to the British Isles, being introduced as an attractive garden plant around two hundred years ago. It grows very rapidly, with its flower stalk growing to heights of 4 metres or more in a few weeks and its leaves forming a very dense covering as shown in the photograph. Giant Hogweed produces vast numbers of seeds (up to 100 000 per plant) allowing it to rapidly colonise whole riverbanks (its usual habitat).

The sap of Giant Hogweed is phototoxic, causing severe blisters and burns if bare human skin is exposed to the sap in sunny conditions.

(i) Using the information provided, state **two** reasons why it is important to restrict the growth of Giant Hogweed.

1. _____

2. _____ [2]

(ii) Giant Hogweed can reduce animal biodiversity along riverbanks. Using the information provided, explain why.

_____

_____

_____

_____

_____ [2]

In an experiment investigating the dispersal of Giant Hogweed plants, the distribution of first year seedlings produced by seeds from two mature plants (**1** and **2**) was analysed. Plant **1** was adjacent to a river's edge and plant **2** was 50 metres from the riverbank. Seedlings arising from these two plants were identified and their position recorded in the summer following seed dispersal. The positions of the two parent plants and their seedlings are shown in the diagram overleaf.

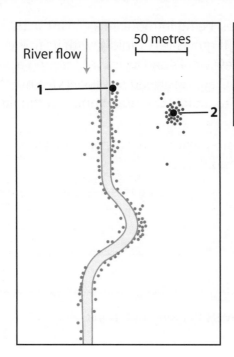

(b) Using the information provided, describe the dispersal and distribution of seedlings from the two parental plants and suggest explanations for their distribution.

_____

_____

_____

_____

_____

_____

_____

_____

_____

_____

_____ [4]

(c) Scientists have tried many methods to restrict the spread of Giant Hogweed, but usually with limited success. These methods have included spraying with herbicides and experimenting with a range of biological control agents.

Investigations using insect species as potential biological control agents have not been successful for several reasons, including the fact that it has been impossible to find an insect species that feeds exclusively on Giant Hogweed.

(i) Apart from being unable to find a biological control agent that feeds exclusively on Giant Hogweed and taking account of the features that a good biological control agent should have, give **three** possible reasons why the species that have been trialled so far have not proved successful.

1. _____

_____

2. _____

_____

3. _____

_____ [3]

However, there are examples of effective biological control in restricting the growth of some plant species and, where successful, biological control is often preferred over chemical pest control.

(ii) Give **two** advantages of biological control compared to chemical pest control.

1. _____

_____

2. _____

_____ [2]

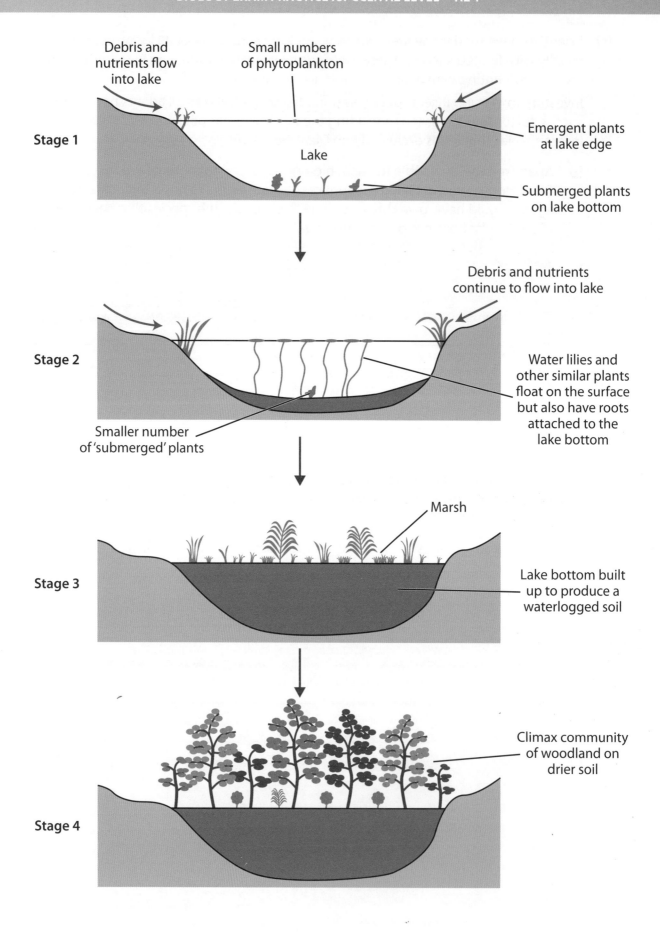

Stage 1

Debris and nutrients flow into lake

Small numbers of phytoplankton

Lake

Emergent plants at lake edge

Submerged plants on lake bottom

Stage 2

Debris and nutrients continue to flow into lake

Water lilies and other similar plants float on the surface but also have roots attached to the lake bottom

Smaller number of 'submerged' plants

Stage 3

Marsh

Lake bottom built up to produce a waterlogged soil

Stage 4

Climax community of woodland on drier soil

6 A large lake is an example of an ecosystem. The diagram opposite shows a typical lake succession showing how lakes can change over thousands of years to become marsh and, in due course, woodland.

Using the information provided, answer the questions below.

(a) **(i)** Give **two** ways in which this lake succession is typical of all successions.

1. _____

_____

2. _____

_____ [2]

(ii) The diagram shows that the lake becomes shallower over time. Give **two** reasons for this.

1. _____

2. _____ [2]

(iii) Suggest **one** reason why floating plants such as water lilies are present at Stage 2 but not Stage 1.

_____

_____ [1]

(iv) Suggest why there are fewer submerged plants at Stage 2 than Stage 1.

_____

_____ [1]

(v) The soil becomes drier as Stage 4 develops. Suggest **one** reason for this.

_____

_____ [1]

(b) The diagram shows that woodland is the climax community. Define the term 'climax community'.

_____

_____

_____

_____ [2]

(c) Eutrophication is a consequence of high levels of nutrients entering lakes.

    (i) Eutrophication leads to reduced biodiversity in a lake. Give **one** reason why. Explain your answer.

       _____

       _____

       _____

       _____

       _____ [2]

    (ii) The process of succession is much faster in a lake following eutrophication. Suggest **one** reason for this.

       _____

       _____ [1]

7 [Section B (essay) type question]

    (a) Succession is a natural process of community development. Describe the changes you would expect to take place in a recently abandoned quarry (a large area of recently exposed rock) in the British Isles, until the ecosystem becomes mature woodland. In your account you should explain the reasons for the changes that take place.   [12]

    (b) The trees which form the canopy in a mature woodland are examples of K-selected species. Describe **three** features of K-selected species and suggest the importance of these features in mature woodland.   [6]

[Complete your account on separate paper]

1 (a) The diagram below represents a pyramid of energy for a food chain. Values are in kilojoules per square metre per year ($kJ\ m^{-2}\ y^{-1}$).

	Energy / $kJ\ m^{-2}\ y^{-1}$
Tertiary consumers	4.4×10
Secondary consumers	3.4×10^2
Primary consumers	3.6×10^3
Producers	5.5×10^4

Note: diagram not to scale

(i) State the trophic level of the secondary consumer.

_____ [1]

(ii) Calculate the percentage of energy of producers that is passed on to primary consumers.
(Show your working.)

_____ % [2]

(iii) Using the information provided, explain why very few food chains involve more than four organisms.

_____

_____

_____ [1]

(b) Using the symbols GPP (gross primary production), NPP (net primary production) and R (respiration), write an equation for NPP.

_____ [1]

2   The diagram below represents a short section of a food chain.

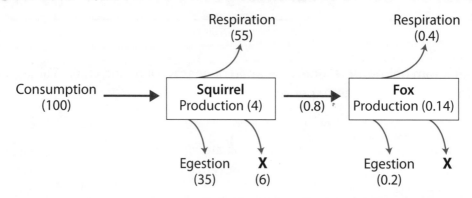

Values are in arbitrary units and represent percentages of the *initial* consumption value for the squirrel. The production value is the percentage of energy available for growth.

(a)   Identify the energy loss labelled **X**.

   _____   [1]

(b)   Calculate the value of **X** in the fox.
      (Show your working.)

                                                                                    _____ % [2]

The table below shows the percentages of consumed energy lost through egestion (faeces) in the squirrel and the fox. The squirrel feeds on nuts, seeds and fruit.

Animal	Energy lost through egestion / %
Squirrel	35
Fox	25

(c)   Give **one** reason for the difference in the two values. Explain your answer.

   _____

   _____

   _____

   _____

   _____   [2]

(d)   Respiratory losses are relatively high in both animals. Suggest **one** reason why.

   _____   [1]

3 The diagram below represents a simplified nitrogen cycle.

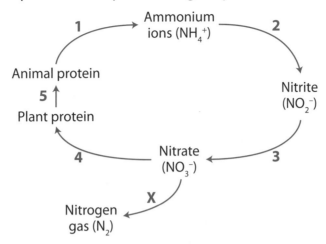

(a) Name the process by which nitrate is absorbed by plant roots (Stage **4**).

_____ [1]

(b) Identify the stage (**1 – 5**) that involves decomposer activity.

Stage _____ [1]

(c) Identify the two stages (**1 – 5**) that involve oxidation reactions.

_____ and _____ [1]

(d) Name the organisms involved in process **X**.

X _____ [1]

4 When quarries are no longer used to provide rock, stones and other products for industry, they are often allowed to return to nature. As this occurs, over many years, the species present change as succession takes place.

(a) Name the type of succession that occurs in quarries.

_____ [1]

(b) The shrub gorse (*Ulex europaeus*) is a relatively long-lived pioneer species common in quarries. Being able to fix nitrogen, gorse can become established in a short time.

(i) Explain why the ability to fix nitrogen enables gorse to be a successful pioneer species in quarries.

_____

_____

_____

_____ [2]

The photograph below shows gorse growing at a quarry edge.

Credit: James Napier

Gorse

(ii) State **one** way in which gorse is different to typical pioneer species.

_____ [1]

The graph below shows how the estimated biomass of gorse and that for the tree species present in a quarry changed over time.

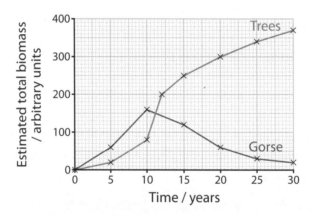

(iii) Calculate the percentage decrease for gorse biomass between 15 and 20 years. (Show your working.)

_____ [2]

It is thought that the decrease in gorse biomass is due to the increasing tree biomass.

(iv) State **two** ways in which the graph supports this conclusion.

1. _____

_____

2._____

_____ [2]

(v) Suggest an explanation for the conclusion that the decrease in gorse biomass is due to the increasing tree biomass.

_____

_____ [1]

5 (a) The burning of large areas of rainforest to provide land for agriculture is thought to contribute significantly to global warming. A common practice in rainforest is 'slash and burn', where a section of the forest is removed by burning and the land used for crops for a number of years before the process is repeated using a new part of the forest.

(i) Describe **two** ways in which this practice contributes to global warming.

_____

_____

_____

_____

_____ [2]

(ii) The removal of rainforest also leads to a reduction in biodiversity. Suggest **one** reason why.

_____ [1]

(iii) Using the information provided, suggest why 'slash and burn' is regarded as being especially harmful to the environment.

_____

_____ [1]

Soil nitrate concentration was monitored over an eight-year period in a section of rainforest which was subsequently cleared by 'slash and burn'. The results of the investigation are shown in the table below.

Year	Mean nitrate content / arbitrary units	Land use
1	45	forest
2	46	forest
3	144	burning
4	91	crops
5	65	crops
6	40	crops
7	19	crops
8	10	crops

(b) Describe and explain the results for soil nitrate concentration.

_____

_____

_____

_____

_____

_____

_____

_____

_____

_____

_____ [5]

(c) Soil nitrate levels are also changed by the process of denitrification.

(i) Describe fully the process of denitrification.

_____

_____

_____ [1]

(ii) Suggest **one** way in which farmers can reduce the rate of denitrification on their land.

_____

_____ [1]

6 Detritus food chains are those involved in the decay and decomposition of dead organic matter. Detritus food chains are particularly active in woodland following leaf fall in autumn. Detritivores, including many species of insects and earthworms, are involved in the initial stages of decay with fungi and bacteria completing the final decomposition and mineralisation process.

(a) Suggest what is meant by the term 'mineralisation'.

_____

_____ [1]

Earthworms feed on dead leaves and other plant debris. The assimilation efficiency of earthworms is very low as up to 99% of all the food ingested is egested as faeces.

(b) Suggest why the proportion of food egested as faeces is so high.

_____

_____

_____ [1]

Earthworms make burrows in the upper levels of the soil and this facilitates other small detritivores gaining access throughout the soil. In addition, the burrows play a part in facilitating the rapid recycling of nitrogen.

(c) Suggest **two** ways in which the presence of earthworms and burrows in the soil facilitate the rapid recycling of nitrogen. Explain your answers.

_____

_____

_____

_____

_____

_____

_____

_____

_____

_____ [4]

Unit A2 2: Biochemistry, Genetics and Evolutionary Trends

Chapter 8 – Respiration

1 State the word(s) that best match(es) the following statements.

- the name given to the stage in aerobic respiration between the production of pyruvate and the production of acetyl co-enzyme A

  _____

- the products of the electron transport chain

  _____ and _____

- the additional oxygen required to metabolise the lactate produced as a consequence of anaerobic respiration

  _____

- the cell location involved in both aerobic and anaerobic respiration

  _____ [4]

2 (a) The Krebs cycle is a focal point of cellular respiration, connecting the link reaction to the electron transport chain. The Krebs cycle is summarised in the diagram below.

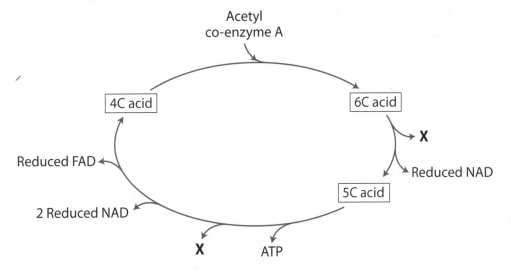

(i) State precisely the location of the Krebs cycle.

_____ [1]

(ii) Identify substance **X**.

_____ [1]

(iii) The diagram shows that for each turn of the cycle, one molecule of ATP is produced. This ATP is produced by substrate-linked phosphorylation.

Suggest what is meant by the term 'substrate-linked' phosphorylation.

_____

_____

_____ [1]

(b) The Krebs cycle is replenished by acetyl co-enzyme A continually combining with a 4C acid to produce a 6C acid.

Describe fully the stage immediately before this which leads to the production of acetyl co-enzyme A.

_____

_____

_____

_____

_____

_____ [3]

(c) The diagram shows that reduced NAD (NADH) is produced at different stages during the cycle.

(i) Describe the role of reduced NAD in the production of ATP in respiration.

_____

_____

_____

_____

_____

_____ [3]

(ii) Using the information provided and your understanding, calculate the number of ATP molecules produced using reduced NAD **from the Krebs cycle** for each molecule of glucose respired.

_____ [1]

3   Anaerobic respiration is respiration which does not involve oxygen.

(a) The main stages of anaerobic respiration in mammals are outlined in the diagram below.

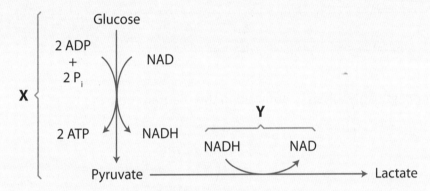

(i) Identify the stage labelled **X** in the diagram.

_____ [1]

(ii) Name the part of the cell where stage **X** takes place.

_____ [1]

(iii) Explain the importance of stage **Y** in anaerobic respiration.

_____

_____

_____

_____

_____ [2]

(b) Anaerobic respiration also takes place in plants.

    (i) State **two** differences between the process of anaerobic respiration in plants and animals.

       1. _____

            _____

       2. _____

            _____ [2]

    (ii) State the advantage of plants being able to respire anaerobically.

       _____

       _____[1]

4 (a) The process of glycolysis is outlined in the diagram below.

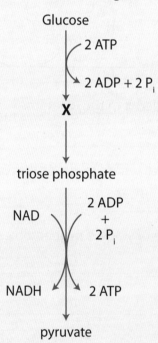

    (i) Name substance **X**.

       _____   [1]

(ii) The diagram shows that ATP is both used and gained in glycolysis. Using the diagram and your understanding, explain why there is a net gain of 2ATP in glycolysis.

_____

_____

_____

_____

_____ [2]

(b) In an investigation, yeast cells were added to a beaker containing 1% glucose as shown in the diagram below.

The cumulative volume of ethanol produced was measured and recorded over time as shown in the graph below.

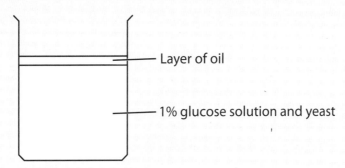

(i) Suggest an explanation for the small amount of ethanol present in the beaker between 22 – 50 hours.

_____

_____

_____ [1]

(ii) Calculate the mean rate of ethanol production per hour between 50 hours and 90 hours.
(Show your working.)

0.3

_____ AU/h^{-1} [2]

(iii) Describe and suggest an explanation for the results between 50 – 100 hours.

_____

_____

_____

_____

_____

_____

_____

_____ [3]

5 (a) Describe what is meant by the term 'respiratory quotient (RQ)'.

_____

_____ [1]

(b) In an investigation into the RQ of yeast cells using different respiratory substrates, the results in the table below were obtained.

RQ Value	Respiratory Substrate
1.45	carbohydrate
0.91	
0.70	

(i) Identify the missing respiratory substrates and complete the table. [2]

(ii) Explain why the respiratory substrate for the 1.45 RQ value could only be carbohydrate.

_____

_____

_____

_____ [2]

(c) Individuals with type-1 diabetes need to inject insulin so that blood glucose can be absorbed into body cells and respired. If they fail to inject insulin, or do not take enough insulin, their cells cannot absorb glucose and therefore the cells respire other respiratory substrates.

The graph below shows the RQ values of a person with type-1 diabetes over a number of hours. This individual did not eat during the period investigated.

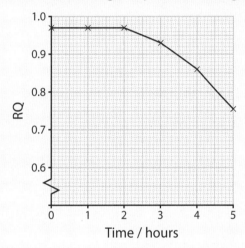

(i) Calculate the percentage decrease in RQ over the period shown.
(Show your working.)

_____ % [2]

(ii) The individual concerned has a record of failing to take enough insulin. Taking account of the information provided, explain the results shown in the graph.

_____

_____

_____

_____

_____

_____

_____

_____ [4]

Chapter 9 – Photosynthesis

1 **(a)** The diagram below summarises the process of photosynthesis.

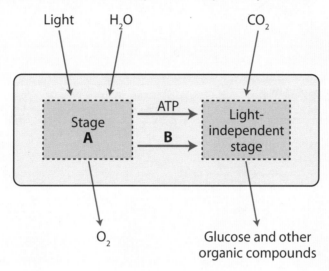

(i) Name stage **A**.

_____ [1]

(ii) Identify substance **B**.

_____ [1]

(iii) Name the substance that carbon dioxide combines with in the
light-independent stage.

_____ [1]

(b) With reference to chlorophyll (and associated pigments), describe what is meant by the
term 'absorption spectrum'.

_____

_____

_____ [1]

2 **(a)** A simplified light-dependent stage of photosynthesis is outlined in the diagram below.

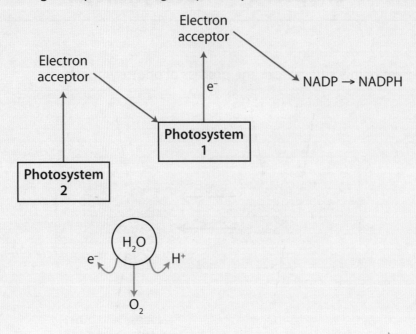

(i) Describe how the electrons (e⁻) and hydrogen ions (H⁺) from the splitting of water (photolysis) are used in the light-dependent reaction.

_____

_____

_____

_____

_____ [2]

(ii) With the letter **X**, indicate on the diagram where ATP is produced. [1]

(iii) Suggest an advantage of two photosystems being involved in the light-dependent stage.

_____

_____ [1]

(b) (i) Describe how the products of the light-dependent reaction are used in the light-independent reaction.

_____

_____

_____

_____

_____

_____

_____

_____ [3]

(ii) State precisely where the light-independent reaction takes place.

_____ [1]

(c) In many plant species, chloroplasts are flattened and orientated in such a way that they gain maximum exposure to light. In certain environmental conditions the orientation of the chloroplasts change, resulting in decreased exposure to light.

Suggest an environmental condition that could cause this change in orientation. Explain your answer.

_____

_____

_____

_____ [2]

3 (a) The light-independent stage of photosynthesis takes place in the chloroplast stroma. This stage does not require light but is dependent on the products of the light-dependent stage. One of these products is ATP.

ATP has two distinct roles in the light-independent reaction. Describe the roles of ATP in the light-independent reaction.

1. _____

_____

2. _____

_____ [2]

(b) In a laboratory investigation, the relative concentrations of ribulose bisphosphate and glycerate phosphate were measured in the chloroplasts of a photosynthesising plant both before and after carbon dioxide was removed from the atmosphere. The results are shown in the graph below.

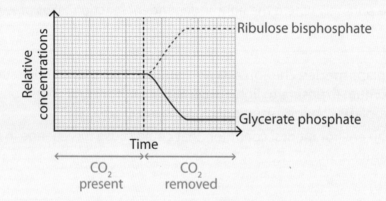

(i) Explain the results shown in the graph following the removal of CO_2.

_____

_____

_____

_____

_____

_____

_____

_____

_____

_____ [4]

Rubisco is an enzyme involved in the light-independent stage. Enhancing rubisco levels in palisade cells by genetic modification can increase photosynthetic rates. However, the increased rubisco concentration only has an effect in certain environmental conditions.

(ii) Suggest the environmental conditions required for increased rubisco concentrations to lead to faster rates of photosynthesis. Explain your answer.

_____

_____

_____

_____

_____

_____ [2]

(c) Although the enzyme rubisco normally catalyses the carboxylation of ribulose bisphosphate (RuBP) to form two molecules of glycerate phosphate (GP), in certain circumstances oxygen (rather than carbon dioxide) combines with rubisco as a substrate molecule.

While this reaction still produces some GP, it also leads to the production of phosphoglycolate (PG). PG needs to be broken down in the cells and this involves a complex series of reactions which are described as being metabolically expensive. The combination of rubisco with oxygen to produce GP and PG and the series of reactions that follow are together described as photorespiration.

(i) Suggest what is meant by the term 'metabolically expensive'.

_____

_____ [1]

(ii) Apart from being metabolically expensive, use the information provided to suggest **one** other reason why plants normally grow better when photorespiration is at a minimum.

_____

_____ [1]

Under normal conditions, most rubisco molecules in a chloroplast combine with carbon dioxide, i.e. 'normal' photosynthesis. However, the relative rate of photorespiration (compared to 'normal' photosynthesis) taking place can increase when oxygen levels rise or carbon dioxide levels fall in the leaf.

(iii) Using the information provided and your knowledge, suggest why scientists predict that the relative rates of photorespiration will decrease in the future.

_____

_____

_____

_____

_____ [2]

4 (a) Describe what is meant by the term 'net photosynthesis'.

_____

_____ [1]

(b) The net volumes of carbon dioxide taken in and used by a plant over a 24-hour period, starting at midnight, are shown in the graph below.

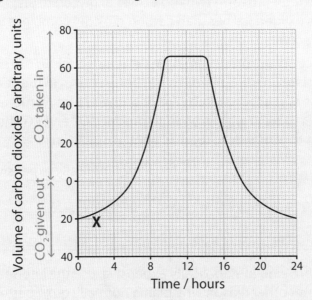

(i) Suggest the environmental factor that is most likely to be limiting the rate of photosynthesis at **X**.

_____ [1]

(ii) Identify the compensation point(s) with the letter **Y** on the graph. [1]

(iii) During which times is there a net loss of carbohydrate in the plant? Explain your answer.

_____

_____

_____

_____

_____

_____

_____ [3]

(c) Many plant species have 'sun' leaves which are adapted to photosynthesise in high light intensities and 'shade' leaves which are adapted for low light intensities (as they are frequently in the shade of the outer 'sun' leaves). For example, 'sun' leaves are usually thicker than 'shade' leaves in the same plant.

(i) Suggest an explanation for 'shade' leaves usually being thinner than 'sun' leaves.

_____

_____

_____ [1]

(ii) Suggest **one** other adaptation of 'shade' leaves.

_____ [1]

(d) The carbon dioxide intake in 'sun' and 'shade' leaves was measured in a tree species at a range of light intensities. The range selected involved the typical light intensities experienced by the species on a summer's day. The results are shown in the graph on the next page.

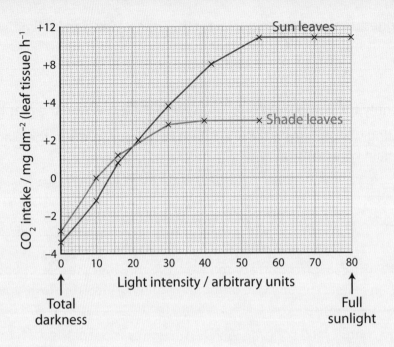

(i) Suggest why there are no results for 'shade' leaves at a light intensity above 55 arbitrary units.

_____

_____ [1]

(ii) Describe and explain the results shown.

_____

_____

_____

_____

_____

_____

_____

_____

_____

_____

_____

_____

_____

_____

_____

_____

_____

_____ [6]

5 Low levels of light, carbon dioxide or temperature can limit the rate of photosynthesis and, equally, an increase in any one of these (within normal limits) will speed up the rate of photosynthesis if the other two factors are not limiting.

However, on a longer time scale, an increase in one or more of these factors can also lead to increased photosynthesis rates through their effect on leaf size and shape.

In an investigation, leaf dimensions (length, width and width/length [W/L] ratio) of Wild Garlic (*Allium ursinum*) plants were measured in 20 sites in each of Ireland, mainland Britain, and mainland Europe. In each site, mean values were based on the measurement of the leaves of 30 plants. The results, including 95% confidence limits, are shown in the table below (vertical bars [in blue] between geographical groupings indicate that the values are not significantly different at $p = 0.05$).

Geographical groupings	Mean temp/°C	Leaf length/mm		Leaf width/mm		W/L ratio	
		mean	+/−95%	mean	+/−95%	mean	+/−95%
Ireland	16	176.5	14.6	46.2	4.4	0.264	0.014
Britain	18	191.1	16.8	51.1	4.4	0.271	0.013
Mainland Europe	20	172.3	11.5	56.8	4.0	0.334	0.017

Carbon dioxide is not likely to change significantly across this geographical range, and light intensities are likely to vary considerably within each grouping. Hence it was hypothesised that any trend in leaf dimensions would most likely be temperature related.

Although mean temperatures in each of these geographical groupings are very variable, summer mean temperatures were estimated as being approximately 16°C in Ireland, 18°C in mainland Britain and 20°C in the parts of mainland Europe involved.

(a) With reference to mean values only, describe the trends (if any) between temperature and leaf **length** and leaf **width**.

_____

_____

_____

_____

_____ [2]

(b) Using the information in the table for leaf dimensions, give the main reason for the change in leaf width/length ratio across the geographical groupings.

_____

_____

_____ [1]

(c) In terms of the presence or absence of significance at $p = 0.05$, summarise the differences in leaf dimensions between the three geographical groupings.

length _____

_____

_____

width _____

_____

_____

W/L ratio _____

_____

_____ [3]

Chapter 10 – DNA as the Genetic Code (Protein Synthesis)

1   Complete the passage below using the most appropriate word(s).

The sequence of bases in the template strand of DNA forms the genetic code, with each group of three consecutive bases known as a _____ coding for an amino acid.

As each base in a DNA sequence is read only once, the code is described as being _____ . As there are more possible combinations of three bases than there are types of amino acid, the code is described as being _____ .

[3]

2   (a)   The diagram below represents an early stage in protein synthesis.

(i)   Name the stage of protein synthesis represented by the diagram.

_____   [1]

(ii)   Name bases **1** and **2**.

1.   _____

2.   _____   [2]

(iii)   State the role of RNA polymerase.

_____

_____   [1]

(b) The partially completed table below shows the numbers of each type of base in a short length of a DNA template strand and the mRNA copied from that DNA.

	Number of bases				
	adenine	guanine	cytosine	thymine	uracil
DNA (template strand)	880	640	741	539	0
mRNA (pre-modification)		741	640	0	880
mRNA (post-modification)	441	709	336	0	790

(i) Complete the table by adding the value for adenine in mRNA pre-modification. [1]

(ii) DNA length can be measured in number of 'base pairs.' Give the length, in base pairs, of the section of DNA analysed in the table.

_____ [1]

(iii) The table shows that the number of bases change as the mRNA molecule is modified. Describe what happens during this modification.

_____

_____

_____

_____ [2]

(iv) Give **one** advantage of the mRNA being modified at this stage. Explain your answer.

_____

_____

_____

_____ [2]

3 (a) Ribosomes are small organelles important in the translation phase of protein synthesis. Approximately 60% of a ribosome is formed of ribosomal RNA (rRNA).

(i) Name the type of molecule that forms the remaining 40% of a ribosome.

_____ [1]

(ii) State precisely the location in the cell where ribosome sub-units are initially assembled.

_____ [1]

(b) The diagram below shows a stage in the synthesis of a polypeptide during translation.

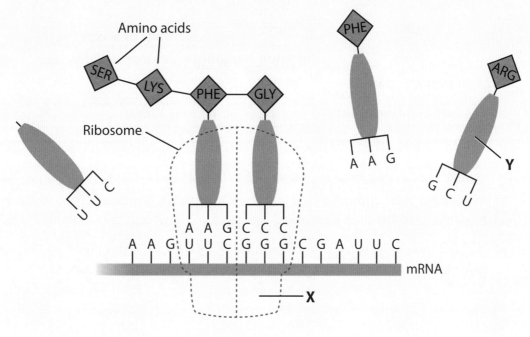

(i) On the diagram, circle and label a codon. [1]

(ii) Name the site on the ribosome labelled **X**.

_____ [1]

(iii) Name molecule **Y**.

_____ [1]

(iv) Using the information in the diagram, describe the sequence of events leading to the attachment of the next amino acid to the polypeptide.

_____

_____

_____

_____

_____

_____

_____

_____

_____

_____

_____

_____

_____

_____

_____

_____ [5]

Ribosomes are often grouped together so that several ribosomes can operate in turn on the same mRNA strand, producing a large number of polypeptide molecules quickly.

(v) Apart from being able to produce large numbers of the same polypeptide quickly, suggest **one** other advantage of ribosomes operating as a group.

_____

_____ [1]

4 It is important to regulate protein synthesis, to prevent the production of proteins in cells where those proteins would be harmful, but also for efficiency. Epigenetic modification is one way in which this regulation takes place.

(a) Define the term 'epigenetic modification'.

_____

_____

_____ [1]

(b) DNA methylation is one example of epigenetic modification. The diagram below shows how methylation takes place.

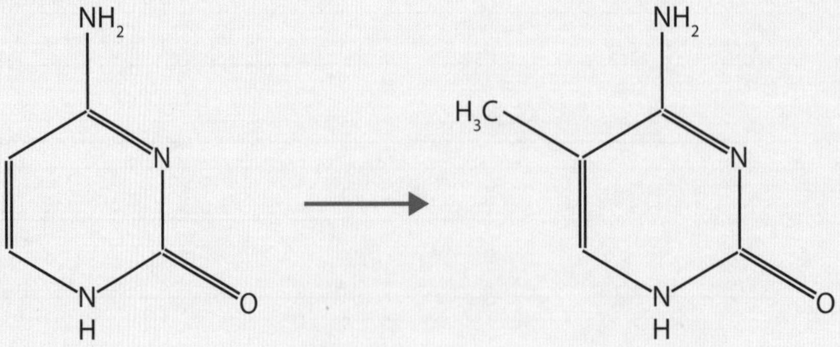

Base **X** before modification

Base **X** after modification

(i) Name the base labelled **X** which may be methylated.

_____ [1]

(ii) State the chemical group added during this modification.

_____ [1]

(iii) Name the stage of protein synthesis affected by methylation.

_____ [1]

Many genes are controlled by sections of DNA which lie immediately before the polypeptide-coding bases. These sections are referred to as promoters as shown in the diagram below.

Analysis of DNA methylation in gene control indicates that it is often the bases in the promotor which are methylated, rather than the bases in the coding section of the gene.

(c) Suggest a possible benefit of this.

_____

_____

_____ [1]

Histone modification is another type of epigenetic modification. Here, the histone proteins are altered in a way which can either increase or decrease gene expression.

(d) Using the information provided and your knowledge, describe **two** differences in outcome between the effects of histone modification and DNA methylation.

1. _____

_____

2. _____

_____ [2]

In the zygote and in early embryo development, many of the epigenetic changes that occurred during the lifetime of the parents are removed, i.e. the 'genetic slate is wiped clean'. This results in the stem cells – the cells which have the potential to develop into cells of any tissue type in the developing embryo and foetus – being relatively free of epigenetic change.

(e) Using the information provided, suggest the importance of this.

_____

_____

_____ [1]

Chapter 11 – Gene Technology

1 Genetically modified microorganisms (GMOs) have been used for many decades. For example, genetically modified bacteria have been producing insulin for medical purposes since the 1970s.

(a) Producing GM bacteria became possible once scientists had worked out how to obtain or produce a gene of interest and then insert that gene into the genome of bacteria.

Restriction endonucleases can be used both for removing a gene of interest and cutting a bacterial plasmid, a common vector, into which the gene can be inserted.

(i) Explain fully the advantage in using the same restriction endonuclease for both functions.

_____

_____

_____

_____

_____ [2]

Alternatively, rather than removing the desired gene itself, mRNA can be obtained from cells and then converted to cDNA. DNA polymerase then uses the cDNA as a template to form double stranded DNA and this is then incorporated into the bacterial genome.

(ii) Name the enzyme used to convert mRNA to cDNA.

_____ [1]

(b) Viruses can also be used as vectors to help transfer genes into the cells of a host organism. However, in addition to their use as vectors, GM viruses have a number of other functions.

Apart from their use as vectors, give **one** function of GM viruses.

_____ [1]

(c) It is important that GMOs are prevented from accidentally escaping from the laboratories and settings in which they are used and potentially causing harm to the environment.

State **two** safety measures that can be used to prevent their transfer into the wider environment.

1. _____

2. _____ [2]

2 (a) The polymerase chain reaction (PCR) is a technique used to produce many copies of a DNA sequence of interest. One cycle of PCR is summarised in the diagram opposite.

(i) **Stage 1** involves separating the double-stranded DNA into single strands. Describe precisely how this is achieved.

_____

_____ [1]

(ii) Name the short sections of DNA (**A**) which hybridise to each of the separated strands of DNA as shown in **Stage 2**.

_____ [1]

(iii) Give **one** function of these short sections of DNA (**A**).

_____

_____ [1]

(iv) PCR takes place in a thermocycler which is programmed to increase and decrease temperature. Explain why this is necessary.

_____

_____ [1]

(v) The diagram shows one cycle of PCR during which the amount of DNA has doubled. Calculate the number of copies of DNA produced after eight cycles.

_____ [1]

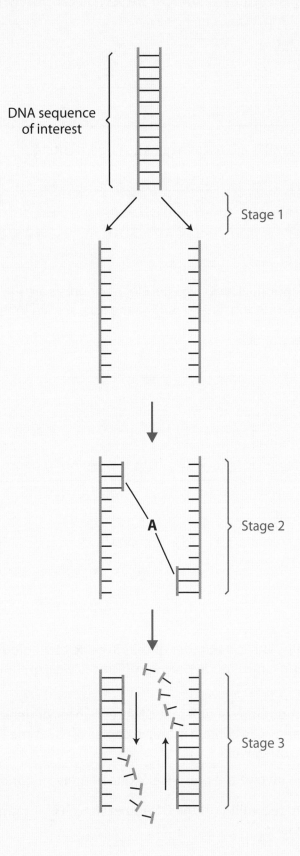

(b) Microsatellite repeat sequences (MRSs) are sections of DNA which are used in genetic (DNA) fingerprinting.

    (i) What is an MRS?

        _____

        _____ [1]

    (ii) Suggest why MRSs are used in genetic fingerprinting.

        _____

        _____

        _____ [1]

    (iii) Restriction endonucleases and gel electrophoresis are each used in the process of genetic fingerprinting. Briefly outline the role of each in this context.

        restriction endonucleases

        _____

        _____

        gel electrophoresis

        _____

        _____ [2]

    (iv) Genetic fingerprinting is used in criminal investigations. Give **one** other example of how it could be used.

        _____ [1]

3 Microarrays ('DNA chips') have a number of uses in gene technology. For example, they can be used to identify single nucleotide polymorphisms (SNPs), mutations, or analyse gene expression (activity).

Microarrays contain thousands of different DNA sequences or genes in microscopic 'wells'. Each 'well' in a microarray can contain multiple copies of the same DNA sequence (with that sequence being in no other well).

Many human diseases involve the presence of one or more mutations in particular genes.

(a) The addition (and recording of) the DNA to each well is automated. Suggest **one** reason why this is necessary.

_____

_____ [1]

(b) Describe how a microarray can be used to identify if an individual has a certain gene mutation.

_____

_____

_____

_____

_____

_____

_____

_____ [4]

(c) Cancer is a consequence of uncontrolled cell division. This can occur for many reasons. For example, a gene important in inhibiting cell division can be too inactive.

The graph below shows the expression level of several genes associated with controlling the rate of cell division in an individual with cancer compared to an individual who is cancer-free. Expression refers to gene activity and can often be measured in terms of molecules of mRNA produced.

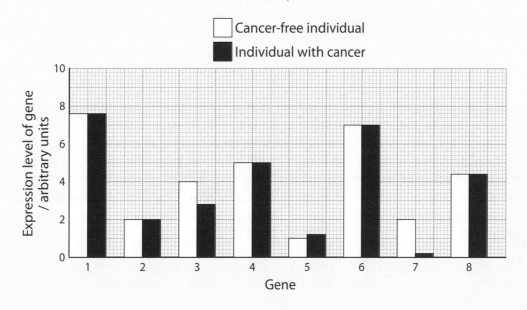

(i) Compare and contrast the results for the individual with cancer and the cancer-free individual.

_____

_____

_____

_____

_____

_____

_____

_____

_____ [3]

(ii) Using the information provided and your understanding, explain how a microarray can provide information about the expression level of a gene.

_____

_____

_____

_____

_____ [2]

4 (a) Gene therapy is increasingly used to treat human medical conditions which have a genetic basis.

Gene therapy has been explored in the treatment of cystic fibrosis (CF) (a condition affecting the lungs, pancreatic duct and other parts of the body), for many years. Individuals with CF have a mutation in a gene controlling ion exchange across cell membranes. A consequence of this mutation is a build-up of mucus in affected parts of the body.

Typically, aerosols containing functional copies of the affected gene are sprayed into the lungs. By using this method, epithelial cells lining the respiratory pathways can take up the functional genes.

However, there have been limits to the success of gene therapy in this context. One issue has been the need to give repeated rounds of treatment.

    (i) Using the information provided and your understanding, suggest why repeated gene therapy applications are necessary in the treatment of cystic fibrosis.

        _____

        _____

        _____

        _____ [2]

    (ii) Apart from the need for repeat applications, suggest **two** reasons why the treatment of cystic fibrosis by gene therapy has not been as successful as initially hoped.

        1. _____

        _____

        2. _____

        _____ [2]

(b) Both liposomes (lipids) and viruses have been used as vectors to deliver functional genes to targeted cells. Over time, viruses have proved to be more effective in this role. However, viruses need to be modified before being used as gene therapy vectors.

    (i) Suggest **one** reason why viruses have proved to be more effective than liposomes as vectors.

        _____

        _____ [1]

    (ii) Suggest **one** way in which viruses are modified before being used as vectors.

        _____

        _____ [1]

Irrespective of the method used for gene delivery, the nuclear membrane has proved to be a significant barrier to getting the functional gene into the nucleus. Research has shown that inserting genes into cell nuclei is more successful if done at a time when the cells are dividing.

    (iii) Suggest a reason for this.

        _____

        _____ [1]

The number of medical conditions that can be treated with gene therapy is continually increasing. Recently, it has been used to treat an inherited mutation which leads to retinal degeneration in the eye; a condition which can lead to blindness. In this treatment, a functional form of the appropriate gene is added to the cells of the retina with the aim of slowing down and (potentially) stopping the retinal degeneration that is a consequence of having a mutation in this gene.

(c) Suggest **one** reason why the eye is proving to be a suitable organ for treatment by gene therapy.

_____

_____ [1]

(d) Gene therapy is most often used where a gene mutation stops a normal protein from being produced.

In some medical conditions due to gene mutations, the problem is that the gene is producing too much of its normal product or producing a different protein that is harmful to cells. In this situation, a technique known as 'gene silencing' can be used. One way to 'silence' a gene is to add drugs which prevent certain messenger RNA (mRNA) molecules from producing polypeptides or protein.

(i) Suggest **one** advantage of targeting the mRNA rather than the gene itself.

_____

_____ [1]

(ii) One way to ensure the correct mRNA molecules are targeted is to use an RNA probe (similar in action to a DNA probe) attached to the drug being used to destroy the mRNA. Describe how an RNA probe will target the appropriate RNA molecule.

_____

_____ [1]

(iii) Explain why an RNA probe would be needed, rather than a DNA probe.

_____

_____ [1]

(iv) Gene 'silencing', as described above, is a treatment that requires regular applications. Using your understanding of protein synthesis, give a reason for this.

_____

_____ [1]

5 Gene mapping and gene sequencing are techniques that together have greatly increased our understanding of the human genome. Gene mapping identifies the position of genes, both in terms of which chromosome carries a gene, but also the position of that gene on that chromosome.

The Human Genome Project (HGP) involved sequencing the human genome, in addition to mapping the genes present, and was a multi-national project lasting many years and costing billions of pounds.

(a) State what is meant by 'sequencing the human genome'.

_____

_____

_____

_____ [2]

(b) Since the working out of the human genome, a number of companies have emerged which will sequence (sections of) an individual's genome for a cost and subsequently provide information on ancestry and genetic health to that individual.

(i) Suggest what is meant by the term 'genetic health'.

_____

_____ [1]

(ii) Suggest **one** advantage and **one** disadvantage of using genetic sequencing data to provide information on future health prospects.

Advantage _____

_____

Disadvantage _____

_____ [2]

Normally these companies sequence a large number (millions) of Single Nucleotide Polymorphisms (SNPs) rather than the entire genome.

(iii) State what is meant by the term 'Single Nucleotide Polymorphism'.

_____

_____ [1]

(iv) Apart from cost, suggest **one** argument for sequencing SNPs only and suggest why it may not be necessary to sequence the entire genome.

_____

_____ [2]

(c) Another consequence of our increased understanding of the human genome is the development of personalised medicine. One aspect of personalised medicine is the development of designer drugs.

    (i) Define the term 'designer drug'.

_____

_____ [1]

The development of personalised medicine and the use of designer drugs has been more limited than many people expected when their use first became possible.

    (ii) Suggest **one** reason for this.

_____

_____ [1]

6 [Section B (essay) type question]

(a) The polymerase chain reaction (PCR), microarrays, 'knockin' and 'knockout' mice have each been important in developing our understanding of the human genome. Describe each of these processes/techniques and how they have helped increase our understanding of the human genome. [12]

(b) Describe what is meant by the term pharmacogenetics and outline the potential benefits and drawbacks of personalised medicine. [6]

[Complete your answer on separate paper]

Chapter 12 – Genes and Patterns of Inheritance

1 (a) (i) With reference to relevant chromosomes, explain the process of sex determination in mammals.

_____

_____

_____

_____ [2]

(ii) Some characteristics in humans are described as being sex-linked. Explain what is meant by the term 'sex-linked'.

_____

_____

_____ [1]

(b) Coat (fur) colour in cats is determined by alleles located on the X chromosome as indicated below.

$$X^b = \text{black fur;} \quad X^o = \text{ginger fur}$$

The $X^b X^o$ genotype results in the 'tortoiseshell' appearance, in which the fur is a mosaic of irregular patches of black and ginger. Sex determination in cats is the same as in humans.

(i) Using the symbols provided, and an appropriate genetic diagram in terms of coat colour and sex, show the expected offspring phenotypic ratio (including sex) that would be produced from a cross between a tortoiseshell and a black cat.

[3]

(ii) Six kittens were produced in a cross between two cats. Three of the litter (offspring) were ginger, two were tortoiseshell and one was black. Identify the **probable** genotype of the parents and use a genetic diagram to show the genotypes and phenotypes of the offspring produced.

[3]

(c) The mosaic of irregular patches of black and ginger in the tortoiseshell cat is a consequence of what is described as X-inactivation early in the embryonic development of a cat. At this early stage, one of the X chromosomes in each cell of a female cat is inactivated (switched off) and it is entirely random which X chromosome in a particular cell is switched off. Therefore, in any one cell in the early embryo, one of the X chromosomes is inactivated yet in a neighbouring cell it could be the other X chromosome which is switched off.

(i) Using the information provided, and in the context of the fur colour gene, identify the chromosome switched off to produce the patches of ginger fur in a tortoiseshell cat.

_____ [1]

(ii) Suggest why the patches of ginger and black fur are of irregular sizes.

_____

_____ [1]

(iii) Name a process which determines the level of expression of genes (or chromosomes) in particular cells.

_____ [1]

2 Gregor Mendel is credited with working out most of the basic principles of genetics. Although unaware of the existence of chromosomes and genes, he was able to work out the presence of genetic features such as dominant and recessive alleles and predict and explain monohybrid and dihybrid crosses.

(a) Explain what is meant by Mendel's second law of inheritance, the law of independent assortment (of factors).

_____

_____

_____ [1]

Most of Mendel's research into genetics involved the breeding of peas (_Pisum sativum_). Peas have many characteristics which are inherited in the traditional monohybrid pattern. These traits include plant height, flower colour, pea shape and colour. The genes for each of these traits is independently inherited.

(b) In peas, round seeds are dominant to wrinkled seeds, and yellow seeds are dominant to green seeds. (R = round; r = wrinkled and Y = yellow; y = green)

(i) Using the symbols above, state the genotype(s) of plants that produce both round and green seeds.

_____ [1]

In a particular cross, two pea plants which produced round and yellow seeds were crossed. One plant was known to be heterozygous for seed shape, but the genotype of the other plant was not known. 312 of the offspring plants produced round and yellow seeds and 95 produced round and green seeds.

(ii) State the offspring ratio that a ratio of 312 : 95 approximates to.

_____ [1]

(iii) Using a genetic diagram, work out the genotypes of the two parents in this cross and the genotypes and phenotypes of the offspring.

[4]

(c) In another genetic cross involving peas, a number of plants heterozygous for both flower colour and seed shape were crossed.

576 seeds (offspring) were produced and these were germinated and allowed to grow the following spring. Later that summer the flower colour and seed shape of these plants were counted and recorded. The results are shown in the observed column in the table below. (Note: purple flower colour is dominant to white flower colour.)

Category	Observed (O)	Expected (E)	(O − E)	(O − E)²	$\frac{(O-E)^2}{E}$
purple flowers and round seeds	327				
purple flowers and wrinkled seeds	117				
white flowers and round seeds	100				
white flowers and wrinkled seeds	32				

(i) State the ratio of offspring expected from a dihybrid cross involving two parents each of which are double heterozygotes.

_____ : _____ : _____ : _____   [1]

(ii) Complete the table and calculate X^2 for these results.

Calculated X^2 value _____   [3]

(iii) On the basis of your calculated X^2 value, state the following:

• the degrees of freedom for the test _____

• the probability value _____   [2]

(iv) State the conclusion that can be drawn from this statistical test.

_____

_____

_____   [1]

(d) Using the information provided, suggest **two** reasons why *Pisum sativum* is ideally suited for genetic investigations.

1. _____

_____

2. _____

_____   [2]

3 **(a)** Marfan Syndrome is a very rare condition that affects around 1 in 5000 people. It is a disease which affects the musculoskeletal system and occurs equally in men and women. 75% of people diagnosed with the disease have inherited it from a parent; in the other 25% it occurs as a spontaneous mutation. For this 25% it most often arises as a mutation during sperm formation.

Marfan Syndrome is caused by the presence of a dominant allele in an autosome.

(i) Using the information provided, suggest why it is normally more accurate to state that Marfan Syndrome is inherited from a 'parent' rather than from 'parents' in those situations where it is inherited.

_____

_____

_____ [1]

(ii) Using the symbols, **M** for Marfan allele and **m** for normal allele, give all the possible genotypes of individuals with Marfan Syndrome.

_____ [1]

(iii) Using a genetic diagram, calculate the probability of a parent heterozygous for the Marfan allele and a parent who does not have the Marfan allele having a child with Marfan Syndrome.

[2]

Data analysed from several countries indicates that there is a relatively strong correlation between the age of the father at birth and the incidence of Marfan Syndrome in his children.

(iv) Using the information provided, explain why the correlation between paternal age and incidence of Marfan syndrome can only ever be a 'relatively strong correlation' and not a '100% correlation'.

_____

_____ [1]

(b) Haemophilia is another relatively rare genetic condition in which the blood fails to clot properly. The gene for haemophilia is located on the X chromosome and it is recessive to the normal allele. The genotypes for males and females without the haemophilia allele can be represented as X^HY and X^HX^H respectively.

(i) Using the symbols provided in this question, give all the possible genotypes of individuals who have neither Marfan Syndrome nor haemophilia, i.e. they do not have either of these genetic conditions.

_____ [1]

(ii) In the space below, complete a genetic diagram to show a cross between a man who carries neither the haemophilia nor the Marfan allele and a female who is heterozygous for both conditions to show the ratio of offspring produced with the possible offspring genotypes and phenotypes. Calculate the ratio only in terms of having or not having each of Marfan Syndrome and haemophilia (i.e. ignore the sex of the individuals when working out offspring phenotypes and ratios).

[5]

4 (a) Explain what is meant by the following genetic terms.

• lethal allele _____

_____

_____

• multiple alleles _____

_____

_____

• epistasis _____

_____

_____ [3]

(b) The normal reddish-brown kernel (fruit) colour in wheat is produced when an enzyme converts a colourless precursor to the final reddish-brown colour. If an appropriate enzyme is not present the kernel remains colourless (white) rather than being converted to the coloured version.

Unusually, two different genes (A and B) on separate chromosomes can produce an enzyme that will catalyse this conversion as shown in the diagram below.

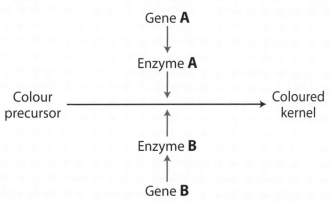

In effect, if a non-functioning form (allele) of either gene A or gene B is present, the other gene can substitute and produce the necessary enzyme. The functional allele of gene A is dominant to the non-functional allele and these are represented by the symbols **A** and **a**. Similarly, the functional allele of gene B is dominant to the non-functional allele and these are represented by the symbols **B** and **b**.

(i) State the phenotype resulting from a genotype of **Aabb**.

_____ [1]

A cross between two wheat plants, one heterozygous for both genes and the other doubly recessive, produced wheat plants, three quarters of which produced coloured kernels and one quarter of which produced colourless kernels.

(ii) Complete a genetic diagram to show how this ratio has arisen. Your diagram should show the genotypes and phenotypes of the offspring.

[4]

1 (a) Complete the table below by naming the biological apparatus/equipment that matches the appropriate description.

Description	Apparatus/equipment
Apparatus used to provide the data required to calculate RQ values	
Strips containing a gradation of antibiotic concentration – these can be used to measure the minimum antibiotic concentration which will kill bacteria	
A special slide used to count the number of unicellular organisms in a suspension	

[3]

(b) Bibliographies have an important role in scientific writing.

(i) Suggest **one** function of a bibliography.

_____

_____ [1]

(ii) State **four** items of information which should be included for each source in a bibliography.

_____

_____

_____ [2]

2 Stock cultures of bacteria can be maintained in the laboratory in nutrient broths, agar (Petri) dishes or agar slopes. The broth and agar contain nutrients essential for bacterial growth.

The diagram below represents bacteria being cultured on an agar slope.

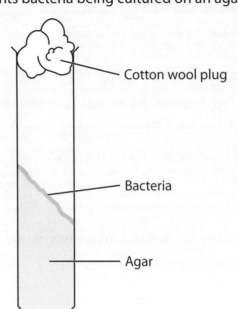

- Cotton wool plug

- Bacteria

- Agar

(a) Using the diagram and your understanding, give **one** advantage of using an agar **slope** to culture bacteria (rather than keeping the tube vertical as the agar sets).

_____

_____

_____ [2]

(b) At periodic intervals, the bacteria must be sub-cultured to maintain a stock (long-term) culture. This means that (some of the) bacteria must be transferred using aseptic technique to fresh agar or broth.

(i) Using the information provided and your understanding, explain why it is necessary to sub-culture bacteria to maintain stock cultures.

_____

_____ [1]

(ii) Describe how you would use aseptic technique to transfer bacteria from a slope culture as shown above to a Petri dish.

_____

_____

_____

_____

_____

_____

_____

_____

_____

_____

_____

_____ [5]

(c) A streak plate can be used to check if a bacterial culture has been contaminated.

  (i) Describe how you would prepare a streak plate.

_____

_____

_____

_____

_____

_____

_____ [3]

  (ii) Following the preparation of a streak plate, suggest how you could conclude if the bacterial culture is contaminated. Explain your answer.

_____

_____

_____

_____ [2]

(d) Many bacterial species can be cultured on agar or broth in a laboratory. Fungal species can also be cultured this way. However, viruses cannot be cultured using the techniques described above. Explain why.

_____

_____

_____ [1]

3 (a) The photograph below shows a longitudinal section (L.S.) through cardiac muscle. The image was taken using a transmission electron microscope (TEM).

Credit: P154/0276, Thomas Deerinck, NCMIR/Science Photo Library

Transverse (T) tubule

X

(i) Identify the muscle band labelled **X**.

X _____ [1]

(ii) State evidence from the photograph which indicates that a light microscope or a scanning electron microscope (SEM) were **not** used in taking this image.

Evidence that a light microscope was **not** used

_____

_____

Evidence that a SEM was **not** used

_____

_____ [2]

The photograph on the previous page is a section of cardiac muscle although it may be difficult to conclude that from this section alone, as skeletal muscle images are very similar.

(iii) State **one** easily recognisable feature of cardiac muscle that is **not** present in this photograph.

_____ [1]

(iv) Suggest **one** function of the transverse (T) tubule labelled in the photograph.

_____

_____ [1]

(b) The TEM image below shows a section through part of a skeletal muscle.

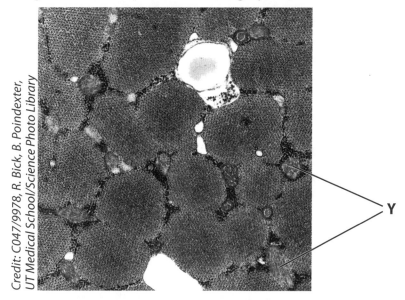

Credit: C047/9978, R. Bick, B. Poindexter, UT Medical School/Science Photo Library

(i) Place a circle around a myofibril on the photograph. [1]

(ii) Name the structures labelled **Y** on the diagram.

Y _____ [1]

(iii) Describe, and suggest an explanation for, the distribution of structures **Y** in this section.

_____

_____

_____

_____ [2]

(iv) Close examination shows that small red 'dots' are visible within the muscle in this section.

Identify these structures and explain their function.

_____

_____

_____

_____

_____ [2]

4 The diagram below represents the side view of a haemocytometer.

(a) On the diagram, draw in the position of the cover slip. [1]

(b) In an investigation, equal masses of yeast were added to 500 cm³ of each of 5% and 10% glucose solutions in separate beakers. Both beakers were kept at 20°C for 3 days. After this time, a sample of yeast was removed from each beaker and added to separate haemocytometers for counting. This process was repeated three times and for each sample replicate the number of yeast cells in five 'squares' was counted, giving 20 replicates in total for each glucose solution.

(i) State **one** variable that should have been controlled when sampling the yeast from the beakers.

_____ [1]

(ii) State **one** precaution that should have been taken when adding the yeast suspension to the haemocytometer.

_____ [1]

(c) After initial observation, it was decided to use type-B squares to count the number of yeast cells.

(i) Explain fully why it would have been decided to use type-B squares (rather than type-A or type-C squares) in this investigation.

_____

_____

_____

_____

_____ [2]

The number of yeast cells in twenty type-B squares was counted for each of the samples. For the beaker with 5% glucose the sample mean was calculated as 12.5.

Type-B squares have an area of 0.04 mm^2 and the distance between the haemocytometer surface and the overlying coverslip is 0.1 mm.

(ii) Using the information provided, calculate the mean number of yeast cells per mm^3 in the 5% glucose solution.

(Show your working.)

_____ mm^{-3} [2]

The mean number of yeast cells per mm^3 for the 10% glucose was calculated as 3700. The data for the two glucose solutions was tested for significance using a t-test.

(iii) State the information required (statistical parameters) required to carry out a t-test.

_____

_____ [1]

(iv) Following completion of the *t*-test, it was found that the difference in mean number between the two glucose solutions was **not** significant. Suggest and explain **one** reason for the relatively similar growth rates of the yeast in the two glucose solutions. (Assume that there were no issues with sampling method, counting or calculation of the mean.)

_____

_____

_____

_____ [2]

5 The diagram below represents a respirometer.

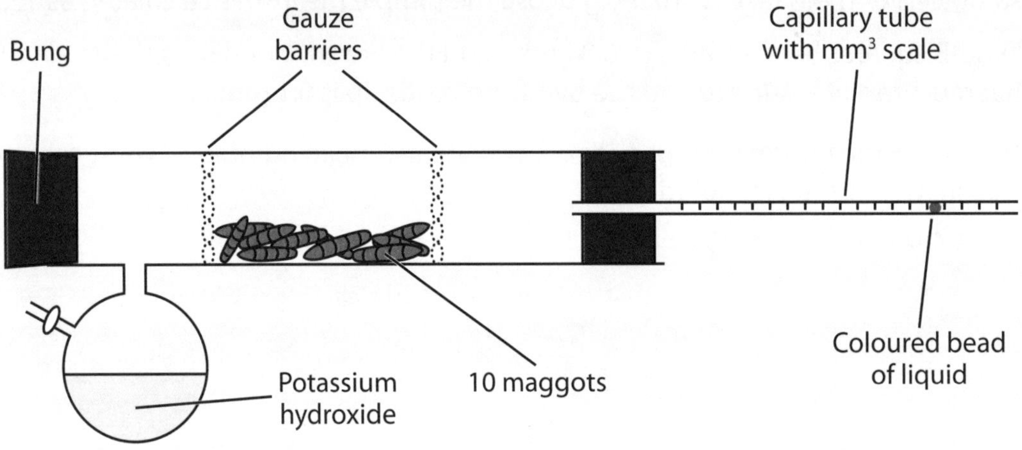

The diagram as shown has been set up for the measurement of the oxygen used in respiration by the maggots.

(a) Following the measurement of oxygen uptake, explain how the apparatus set-up would be changed to calculate the volume of carbon dioxide produced by the maggots.

_____

_____ [1]

(b) Suggest **two** distinct reasons why 10 maggots were used in this investigation rather than just one.

_____

_____

_____

_____ [2]

(c) In the investigation, the total oxygen consumption over a 10-minute period was calculated as 182 mm³.

    (i) Calculate the value for the oxygen consumed per maggot per minute.

        _____ mm³ min⁻¹ [1]

Following the calculation of total carbon dioxide production over the same time period, a respiratory quotient (RQ) value of 0.91 was calculated for the maggots.

    (ii) Using the information provided, calculate the volume of carbon dioxide produced over the same time period.

        _____ mm³ [2]

6 During the light-dependent stage of photosynthesis, photolysis (water-splitting) occurs. The hydrogen released reduces NADP to form NADPH, a product required in the light-independent stage.

DCPIP is a redox indicator which is coloured blue when oxidised but colourless when reduced.

In an experiment investigating the light-dependent stage, a suspension of chloroplasts was prepared by grinding fresh lettuce leaves in a buffer solution and then separating the chloroplasts from other leaf material by centrifugation.

(a) Centrifugation was used initially to separate and remove cell nuclei before the chloroplasts could be isolated.

    (i) Following the removal of the nuclei, describe how and why centrifugation will separate chloroplasts from other cell material.

_____

_____

_____

_____

_____ [2]

(ii) Suggest **one** advantage of using isolated chloroplasts rather than macerated leaf tissue.

_____

_____

_____ [1]

(b) Following the isolation of the chloroplasts, three test tubes were set up as described in the table below. The colour of the tubes at the start of the investigation and after 20 minutes is included.

Tube	Test tube set-up	Light regime	Colour	
			at start	**after 20 minutes**
A	buffer and DCPIP	bright light	blue	blue
B	chloroplast suspension and DCPIP	darkness	blue-green	blue-green
C	chloroplast suspension and DCPIP	bright light	blue-green	

(i) State the function of tube **A** in this investigation.

_____

_____ [1]

(ii) Explain the result for tube **B**.

_____

_____

_____

_____ [2]

(iii) Predict the result you would expect for tube **C**. Explain your answer.

_____

_____

_____

_____

_____ [2]

7 The photograph below shows part of a sycamore tree in early autumn.

Credit: James Napier

X

Y

In autumn, many deciduous trees withdraw their most valuable leaf pigments into their branches and stems. Pigments present in a leaf or leaves at any time can be identified using chromatography.

(a) Describe how you would produce a pigment extract suitable for use in chromatography.

_____

_____

_____

_____

_____

_____

_____ [3]

(b) An investigation compared the pigments present in leaves taken from position **X** in the photograph and those from position **Y**.

    (i) Suggest **one** variable which would have had to be controlled when preparing the extracts for the two groups of leaves.

_____ [1]

(ii) Predict the results you would expect, both in terms of pigments present and the density of pigments present between the two groups of leaves following chromatography.

_____

_____

_____

_____

_____

_____ [2]

(iii) The photograph shows that all the leaves on the same tree do not change colour at the same time. Suggest **one** reason for this.

_____

_____ [1]

(c) A teacher with many years' experience observed that when carrying out the chromatography of plant pigments, the solvent front usually failed to extend more than half-way up the chromatogram, irrespective of the length of running time.

(i) Suggest **one** effect of this on the outcome of chromatography investigations.

_____

_____ [1]

(ii) Apart from changing the type of solvent used, suggest **one** other way to increase the distance over which the solvent will flow.

_____

_____ [1]

8 (a) A gel electrophoresis tank is represented by the diagram below.

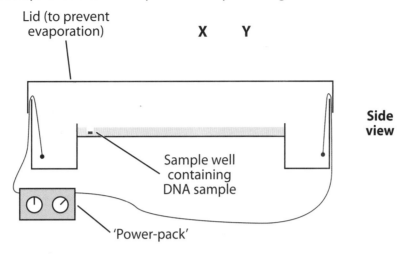

(i) On the diagram, draw a line from the letter **X** to label the cathode (negative electrode). [1]

(ii) On the diagram, draw a line from the letter **Y** to label the buffer solution. [1]

(iii) Apart from maintaining a constant pH, give **one** function of the buffer in this apparatus.

_____ [1]

(b) In an investigation, four batches of identical sections of DNA were each incubated with restriction endonuclease enzymes at 30°C. Following incubation, the four batches of digested DNA were added to the four wells (**A – D**) in a gel electrophoresis tank. The diagram below represents an aerial view of the agarose gel following the migration of DNA fragments. (The diagram only shows the position of the fragments for wells **A** and **B**.)

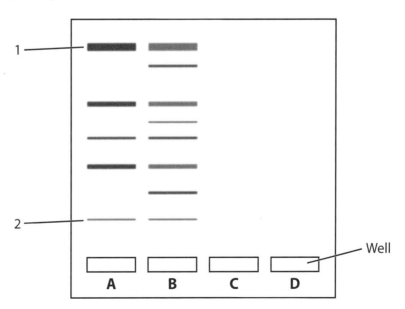

(i) In terms of size and density of fragments, explain the difference between the bars **1** and **2** in lane **A**.

_____

_____

_____

_____

_____ [2]

(ii) Compare and contrast the number and distribution of bars in **lane B** compared with **lane A** and suggest an explanation to account for your answer.

_____

_____

_____

_____

_____

_____

_____ [3]

(c) Restriction enzymes, as with virtually all enzymes, are sensitive to temperature. Suggest what would be seen in lane **C** had the DNA and restriction enzyme mix been subjected to a temperature well above the enzymes' optimum. Explain your answer.

_____

_____

_____

_____ [2]

9 The photograph below shows cells in a moss leaf. Magnification is ×500.

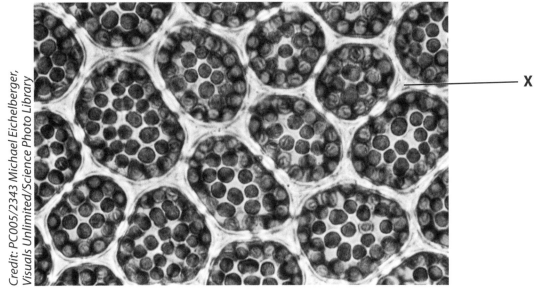

X

(a) Name the cell component labelled **X**.

_____ [1]

(b) Name the type of microscope used to take this photograph.

_____ [1]

(c) Moss 'leaves' are undifferentiated. Suggest what 'undifferentiated' means in this context.

_____

_____

_____ [1]

(d) The chloroplasts in the photograph appear to be more densely arranged around the edge of the cells compared to the centre. Suggest a reason for this. Explain your answer.

_____

_____

_____

_____ [2]

10 (a) The drawing below represents an epidermal layer following the leaf scrape of a grass leaf, as viewed down a microscope.

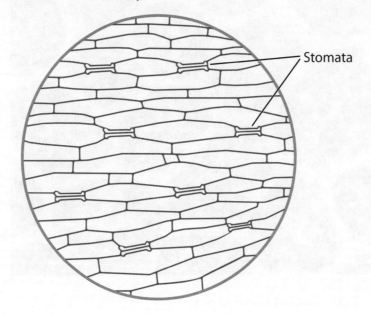

Stomata

(i) When this section was viewed under the microscope no nuclei were visible. Suggest **one** reason why.

_____ [1]

(ii) Suggest why the stomata are shown closed.

_____

_____ [1]

(b) In another leaf scrape, when viewed under the microscope, part of the leaf scrape appeared green and it was difficult to focus on individual cells. Suggest why it was difficult to focus this section.

_____

_____ [1]

(c) In an investigation to compare number of leaf hairs on the upper and lower leaf surfaces of leaves in a grass species, the number of leaf hairs observed in the field of view at low power was counted.

Five leaves were sampled, and five different fields of view were used for each leaf surface to give an overall sample size of 25 for each leaf surface.

Statistical parameters for the two leaf surfaces are shown on the following page.

	Upper leaf surface	Lower leaf surface
Sample size	25	25
Mean number of leaf hairs	8.7	13.0
Standard deviation (error) of the mean	0.81	1.21

(i) Calculate the value of *t* using the data in the table above.
(Show your working.)

_____ [2]

(ii) State the probability for your calculated *t* value.

_____ [1]

(iii) Comment on the outcome of your statistical test and suggest a possible explanation.

_____

_____

_____

_____

_____

_____ [3]